really easy keyboard

BUMPER CHRISTMAS BOOK

Wise Publications
part of The Music Sales Group
London / New York / Paris / Sydney / Copenhagen / Berlin / Madrid / Hong Kong / Tokyo

really easy keyboard

BUMPER CHRISTMAS BOOK

Wise Publications
part of The Music Sales Group
London/New York/Paris/Sydney/Copenhagen/Berlin/Madrid/Hong Kong/Tokyo

YOUR KEYBOARD

Although keyboards vary from make to make and model to model, they all have the same basic features:

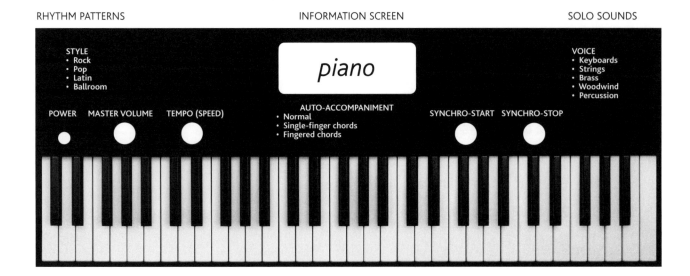

RHYTHM PATTERNS   INFORMATION SCREEN   SOLO SOUNDS

Power (mains)

This turns the keyboard on or off. Most keyboards can run on batteries or from the mains, using a suitable transformer, which is usually supplied with your keyboard.

Master Volume

This controls the overall 'loudness' of the instrument. It is either in the form of a slider, button or knob, which can be set anywhere from minimum to maximum.

Auto-accompaniment

This feature adds an automatic accompaniment to your melody, which you can use in various different ways.

Tempo (Speed)

This controls the speed of the accompaniment rhythm. It can be set anywhere from minimum to maximum, or may display an exact tempo, e.g. ♩ =112. The number displayed is the number of beats per minute, and varies between about 45 to about 220.

Synchro-start

This button activates the auto-accompaniment and synchronises it to when you start playing.

Rhythm or Style

This feature adds a drum rhythm to your melody. You can choose between a number of different styles, e.g. rock, pop, Latin, swing etc.

Voices or Solo Sounds

These might be grouped in different 'types' of voice, e.g. strings, woodwind, or they may be grouped by instrument, depending on how many different voices your particular keyboard offers. They add colour and interest to your melodies.

Information Screen

Most modern keyboards incorporate a digital screen which provides information about which settings you are using, e.g: which voice and rhythm you have selected, and whether you are using auto-accompaniment.

Voice settings

The voices (solo sounds) on your keyboard might be divided into general categories, such as keyboards, woodwind, brass, strings, and so on (a bit like an orchestra). If, for example, you want to use a piano sound, go into keyboards, press 01 on the number pad (01 is an almost universal number set up for a basic piano sound) and the piano sound will appear on the screen.

Rhythm settings

There will be many different rhythm patterns (sometimes called styles) available on your keyboard. Like voices, rhythms will probably be subdivided into categories. Typical rhythm categories are rock, pop, ballroom and Latin.

In your rock category, select one of the rock variations, for example 'rock pop', and press start. Listen to this rhythm pattern for a few moments, then try speeding it up or slowing it down using your tempo control. Try other rock variations, or totally different rhythms, such as quickstep (probably in the ballroom category) or bossa nova (probably in the Latin category).

Now, instead of the start button, select synchro, or synchro-start. Play any note in the lower register (the lower half of the keyboard) and the rhythm section will start automatically. Press synchro again and the rhythm will stop.

See your owner's manual for specific details.

READING NOTATION

To perform the songs in this book, you will need to play the chords with your left hand and the melody with your right. The chords you need to play are written above the notation and the shapes for these chords are shown at the beginning of each song.

Before you start to play, make sure you have the correct voice, rhythm and tempo settings.

Here are some helpful reference notes for reading the notation:

Notes values and rests

The note value tells you the duration of a note—how many beats it lasts. When read in sequence, note values show the rhythm of the music.

Each has its own rest, which indicates a silence for the equivalent duration.

symbol	name	duration	rest
o	semibreve	4 beats	—
♩ or ᴾ	minim	2 beats	▬
♩ or ᶠ	crotchet	1 beat	⁊
♪ or ♭	quaver	½ beat	⁊
♬ or ♭	semiquaver	¼ beat	⁊

Sharps, flats and naturals

♯ A **sharp** sign raises the pitch of a note by a semitone to the very next key on the right.

♭ A **flat** sign lowers the pitch of a note by a semitone to the very next key on the left.

♮ A **natural** sign cancels the effect of a sharp or a flat, representing the unaltered pitch.

A **key signature** is written at the start of each line of music. It tells us which notes should be played as *sharps* or *flats* and saves writing a ♯ or ♭ sign every time these notes appear.

Time signatures

The **time signature** appears after the key signature at the beginning of the music.

The *upper figure* shows the number of beats in each bar and the *lower figure* tells us what note duration gets one beat.

$\frac{4}{4}$ or **C** = four crotchet beats per bar
(also called common time)

$\frac{3}{4}$ = three crotchet beats per bar

$\frac{2}{4}$ = two crotchet beats per bar

$\frac{2}{2}$ or **¢** = two minim beats per bar
(also called cut common time)

$\frac{6}{8}$ = six quaver beats per bar

$\frac{12}{8}$ = twelve quaver beats per bar

Repeat signs and other navigation marks

‖: This is an end **repeat sign**, which tells you to repeat back from the beginning, or from the start repeat:‖:

[1.] [2.] **First-** and **second-time bars** are used to indicate passages in a repeated section that are only performed on certain playings.

D.C. *(Da Capo)* tells you to repeat from the beginning.

D.C. al Fine *(Da Capo al Fine)* tells you to repeat from the beginning to the end, or up to **Fine** .

D.S. *(Dal Segno)* tells you to repeat from the sign 𝄋 .

D.S. al Coda *(Dal Segno al Coda)* tells you to repeat from the sign 𝄋 and then, when you reach **to Coda** ⊕, you should jump to the Coda, marked ⊕ **Coda** .

NOTE GUIDE

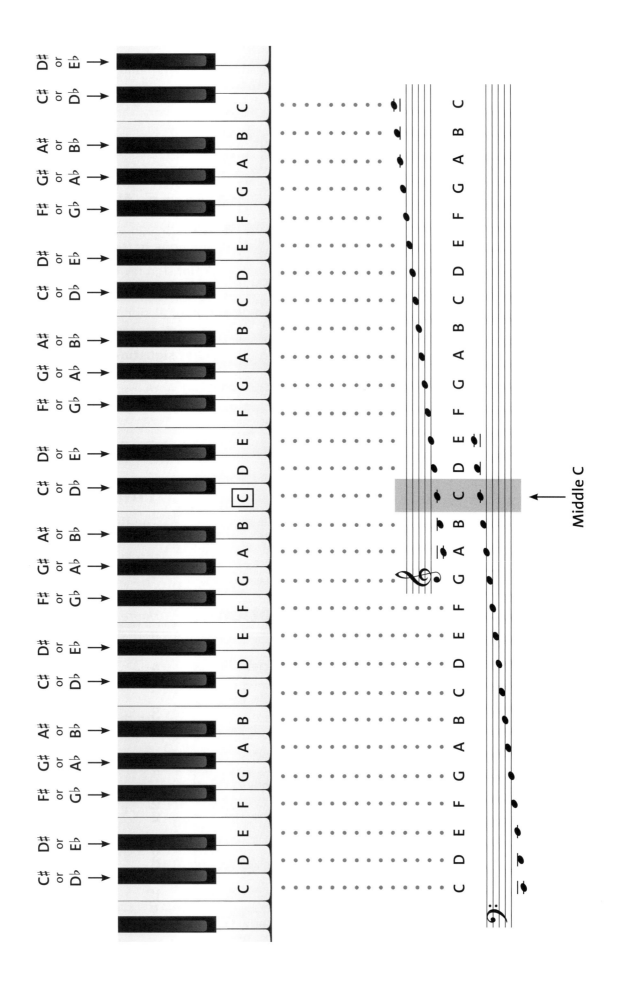

Middle C

Published by
Wise Publications
14-15 Berners Street,
London W1T 3LJ, UK.

Exclusive Distributors:
Music Sales Limited
Distribution Centre, Newmarket Road,
Bury St Edmunds, Suffolk IP33 3YB, UK.
Music Sales Pty Limited
Level 4, Lisgar House,
30-32 Carrington Street,
Sydney, NSW 2000 Australia.

Order No. AM1013276
ISBN 978-1-78558-825-9

Music processed by Sarah Lofthouse, SEL Music Art Ltd.
Music arranged by Fiona Bolton.
Edited by Louise Unsworth.

Printed in the EU.

A Spaceman Came Travelling

Words & Music by Chris de Burgh

It was second time lucky for De Burgh's 'A Spaceman Came Travelling'. Piggy-backing on the success of his 'Lady In Red', it was re-released a decade after it first saw the light of day. It became only a modest hit then, but remains a perennial favourite.

Hints & Tips: Try to hold the semibreves (whole notes) and minims (half notes) in the right hand for their full value.

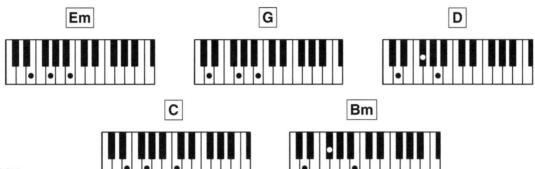

Voice: **Fantasy**

Rhythm: **Soft 8-beat**

Tempo: ♩ = 80

Steadily

A space - man came trav - 'lling on his ship from a - far, 'twas

light years of time since his mis - sion did start; and o - ver a vil - lage, he

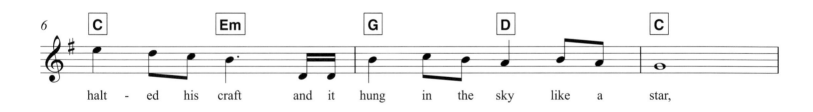

halt - ed his craft and it hung in the sky like a star,

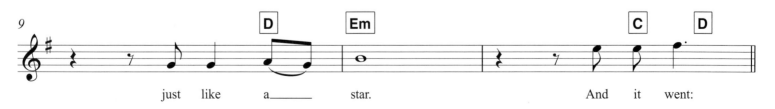

just like a_____ star. And it went:

A Winter's Tale

Words & Music by Mike Batt & Tim Rice

David Essex was well served by songwriters Mike Batt and Tim Rice. Writing to order, they came up with 'A Winter's Tale' in just 48 hours. It was a big Christmas success for Essex, going on to reach the No. 2 spot in January 1983.

Hints & Tips: Take care to count the full length of the long notes in bars 4, 13, etc. as well as the rests at the beginning of the following bars to make sure you don't skip any beats. It might feel like a long time until your next melodic entry but it is important to stay in time with the accompaniment.

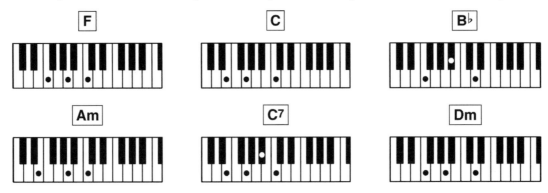

Voice: **Oboe**

Rhythm: **Soft 8-beat**

Tempo: ♩ = 84

Moderately

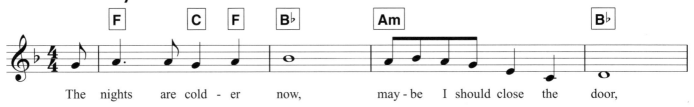

The nights are cold-er now, may-be I should close the door,

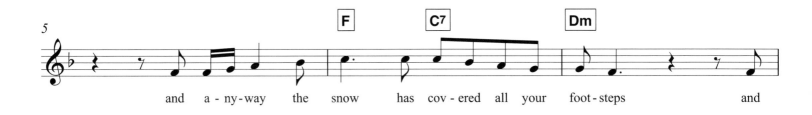

and a-ny-way the snow has cov-ered all your foot-steps and

I can fol-low you no more. The fire still burns at night, my

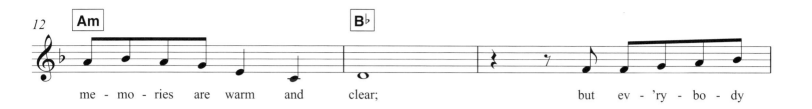

me - mo - ries are warm and clear; but ev - 'ry - bo - dy

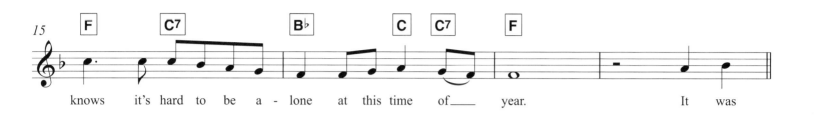

knows it's hard to be a - lone at this time of___ year. It was

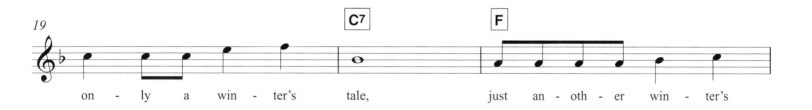

on - ly a win - ter's tale, just an - oth - er win - ter's

tale, and why should the world take no - tice of

one more love that's failed? It's a love that can nev - er

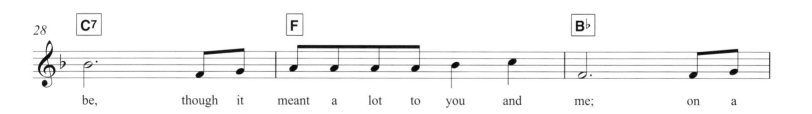

be, though it meant a lot to you and me; on a

slowing

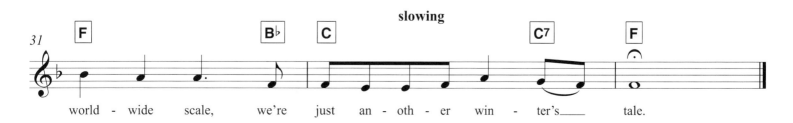

world - wide scale, we're just an - oth - er win - ter's___ tale.

All I Want For Christmas Is You

Words & Music by Mariah Carey & Walter Afanasieff

One of Mariah Carey's biggest ever hit singles, this song reached No. 2 in the UK in December 1994.
It was taken from the album *Merry Christmas*, which mixed original material with traditional seasonal songs.

Hints & Tips: Take your time over the first 16 bars, playing the melody freely. Don't start the
keyboard rhythm until bar 18, perhaps using a one-bar 'fill' to lead you into the verse.

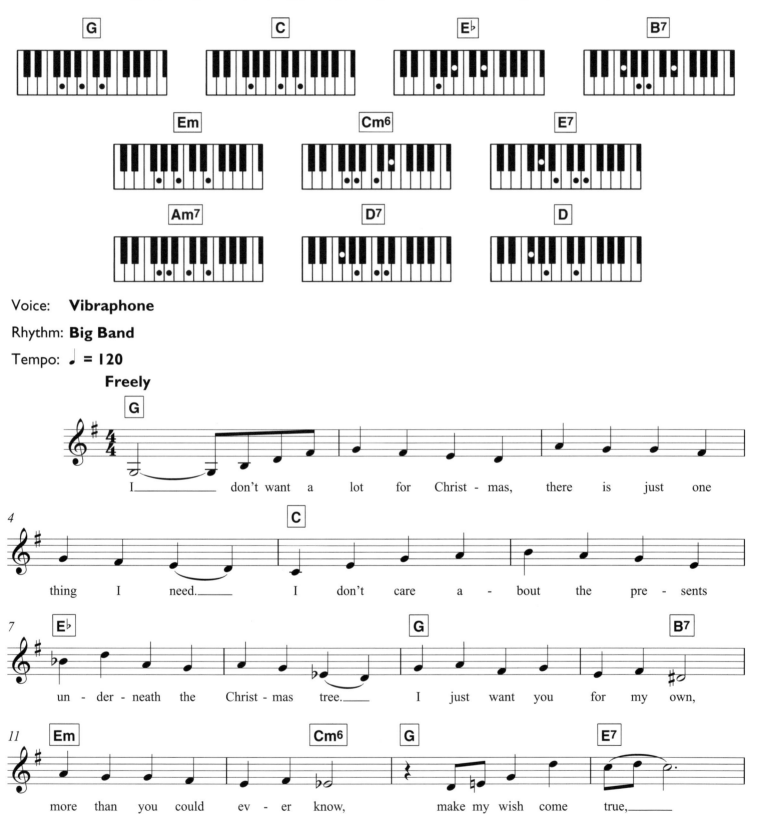

Voice: **Vibraphone**

Rhythm: **Big Band**

Tempo: ♩ = 120

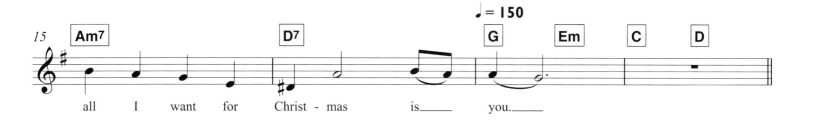

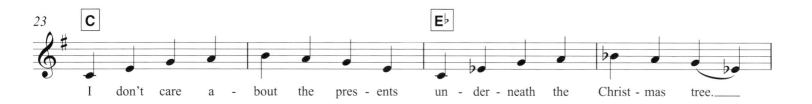

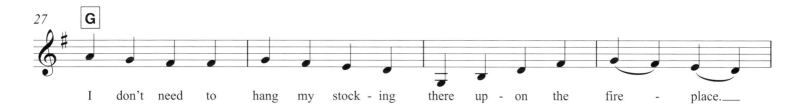

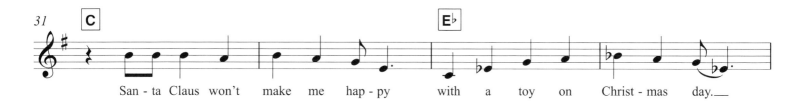

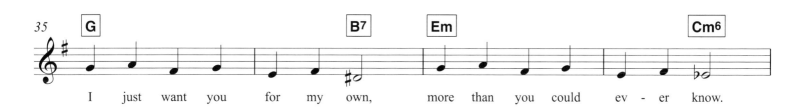

Angels From The Realms Of Glory

Words by James Montgomery
Music: Traditional

James Montgomery wrote over 400 hymns and this is probably his best-known. He also found time to pursue a career as an editor of a newspaper called the *Sheffield Iris* for 32 years. He was imprisoned twice, once for printing a song in commemoration of the fall of the Bastille, and then for giving an account of a riot in Sheffield!

Hints & Tips: Practise the chorus slowly at first, keeping your fingertips close to the keys to create a flowing movement through the descending quavers.

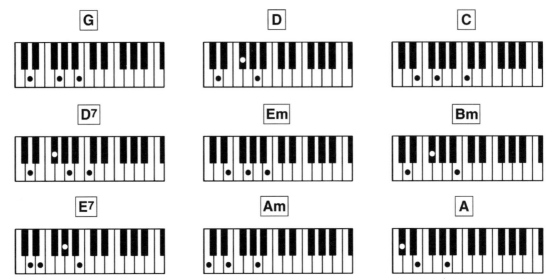

Voice: **Chorus**

Rhythm: **Baroque**

Tempo: ♩ = 120

Lively

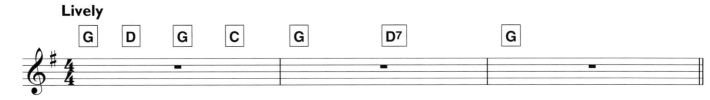

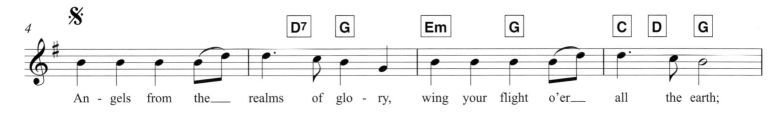

An - gels from the___ realms of glo - ry, wing your flight o'er___ all the earth;

to Coda ⊕

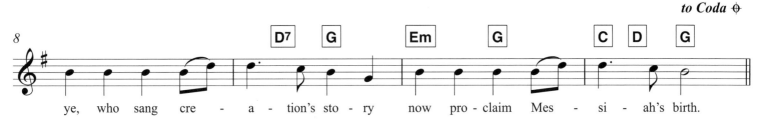

ye, who sang cre - a - tion's sto - ry now pro - claim Mes - si - ah's birth.

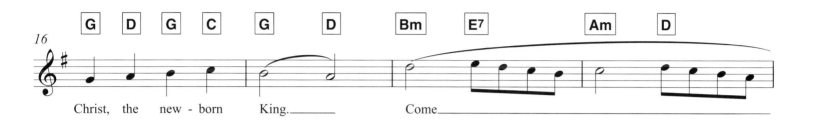

D.S. al Coda

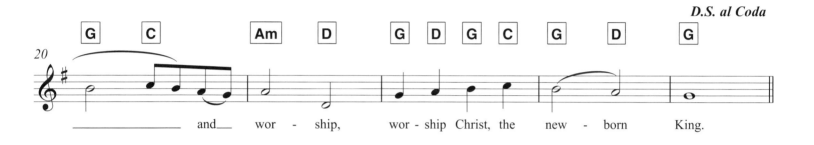

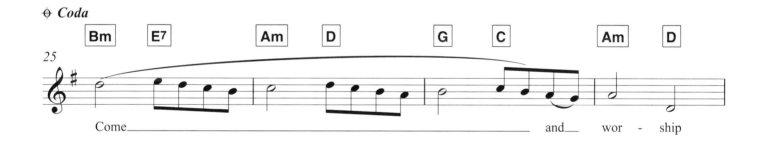

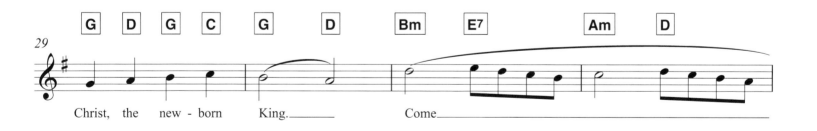

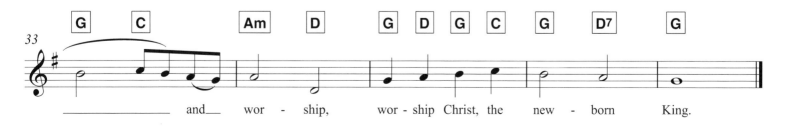

Away In A Manger

Words: Traditional
Music by William Kirkpatrick

There are two melodies for this carol, this one being the better-known. It was first published in 1885.

Hints & Tips: Think about how you can create a contrast between the first and second halves of this carol before you start to play; perhaps choose a different voice or change the dynamic to retain the listener's interest.

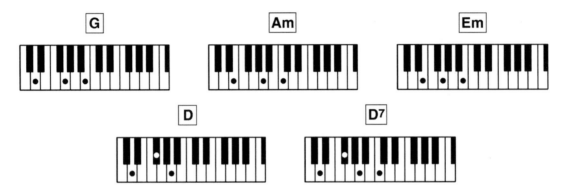

Voice: **Flute**

Rhythm: **Waltz**

Tempo: ♩ = 76

Gently

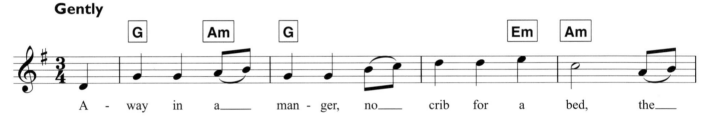

A - way in a___ man - ger, no___ crib for a bed, the___

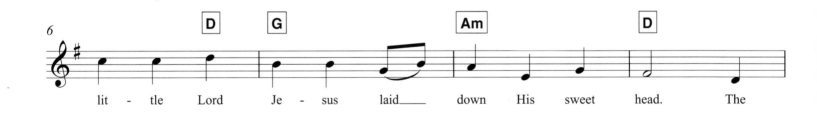

lit - tle Lord Je - sus laid___ down His sweet head. The

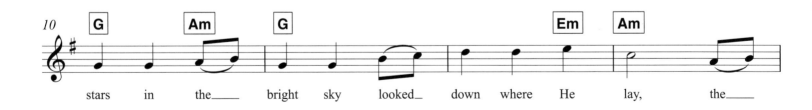

stars in the___ bright sky looked_ down where He lay, the___

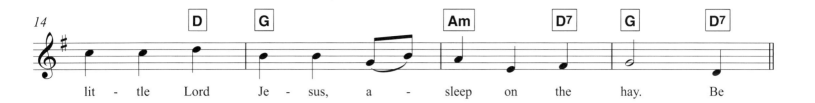

lit - tle Lord Je - sus, a - sleep on the hay. Be

near me Lord___ Je - sus; I___ ask Thee to stay close___

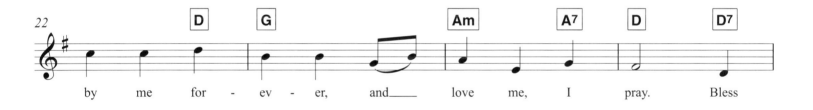

by me for - ev - er, and___ love me, I pray. Bless

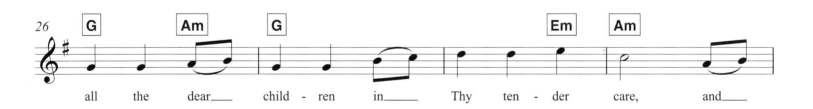

all the dear___ child - ren in___ Thy ten - der care, and___

take us to Hea - ven to___ live with Thee there.

Blue Christmas

Words & Music by Billy Hayes & Jay Johnson

A hit for country artist Ernest Tubb in 1950, this song was recorded by Elvis Presley in 1957 for a seasonal album. Seven years later, RCA released Elvis' version as a single, coupled with 'White Christmas'. Since then, it has always been associated with The King.

Hints & Tips: Play this melody with slightly swung quavers to convey the swagger of Elvis Presley's classic rendition. Listen to a recording to give yourself the flavour of the song if you aren't already familiar with it.

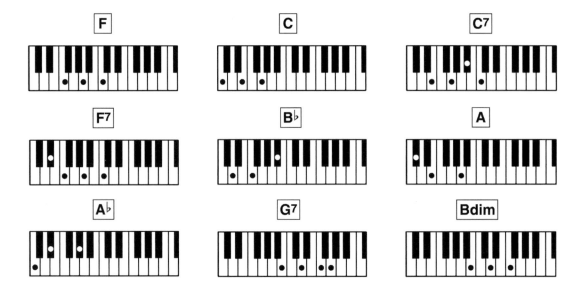

Voice: **Steel Guitar**

Rhythm: **Country Ballad**

Tempo: ♩ = 92

In a relaxed manner

I'll have a blue Christ-mas with - out you.

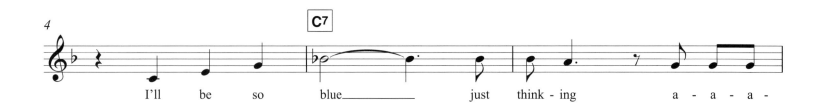

I'll be so blue just think-ing a - a - a -

- bout you. De - co - ra - tions of red on a

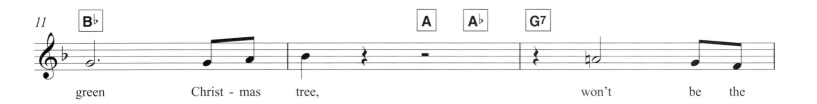

green   Christ - mas   tree,   won't   be   the

same,   dear,_____   if   you're   not   here   with   me.   And   when   the

blue   snow - flakes   start   fall - ing,_____

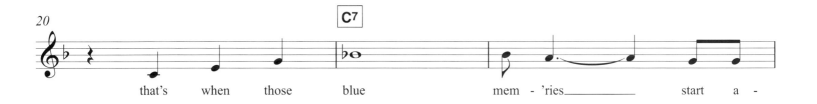

that's   when   those   blue   mem - 'ries_____   start   a -

-call - ing._____   You'll   be   do -   in'   al -

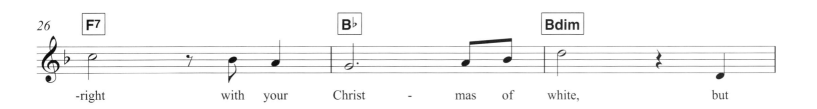

-right   with   your   Christ -   mas   of   white,   but

I'll   have   a   blue,   blue,   blue   Christ - mas._____

The Coventry Carol

Traditional

Dating from the 16th century, this ancient melody was sung in Coventry as part of a play
called *The Pageant Of The Shearmen And Tailors*. It also contains a well-known example of the
'Picardy Third' which is the practice of ending a piece that is in a minor key on a major chord.

**Hints & Tips: Unlike most other Christmas carols, this song has a melancholy air about it.
Choose a accompaniment that works at the slower tempo it demands.**

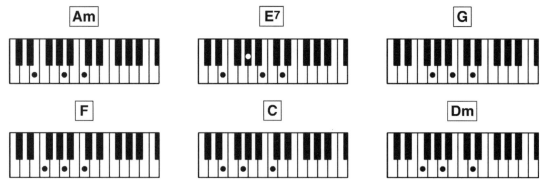

Voice: **Oboe**

Rhythm: **Pop Waltz**

Tempo: ♩ = **76**

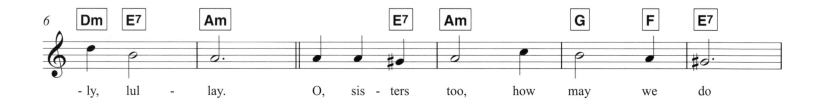

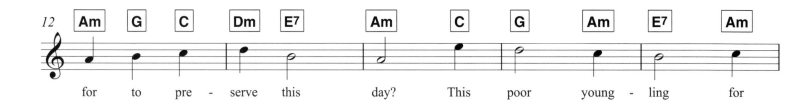

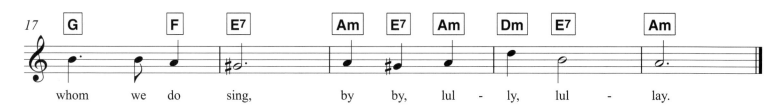

Deck The Halls

Traditional

This is a secular carol with a traditional, probably Welsh, tune. Mozart allegedly
used the melody in the 18th century for one of his violin sonatas.

Hints & Tips: Contrast the exuberant first phrase by reducing the dynamic to piano at bar 12 and
gradually growing in strength (*crescendo*) over the next four bars to a triumphant final phrase.

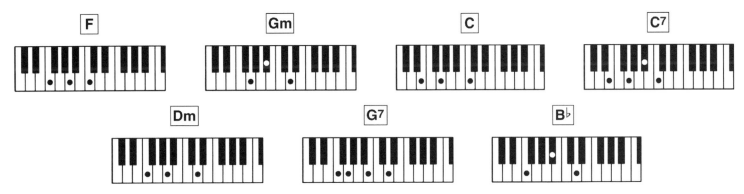

Voice: **Trumpet**

Rhythm: **March**

Tempo: ♩ = 118

Brightly

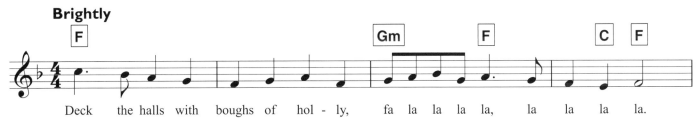

Deck the halls with boughs of hol-ly, fa la la la la, la la la la.

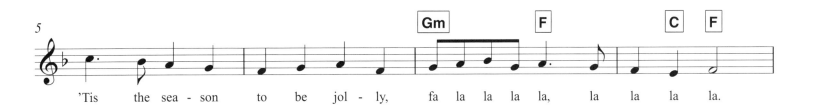

'Tis the sea-son to be jol-ly, fa la la la la, la la la la.

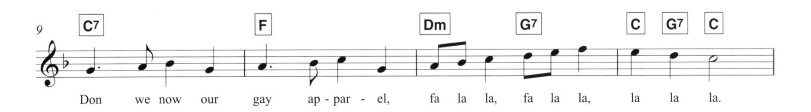

Don we now our gay ap-par-el, fa la la, fa la la, la la la.

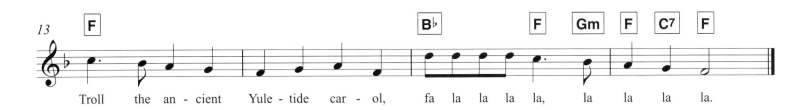

Troll the an-cient Yule-tide car-ol, fa la la la la, la la la la.

Ding Dong! Merrily On High

Words by George Woodward
Music: Traditional

The melody to this song is very old, dating from the 16th century, however the lyrics were added much later, in the early 20th century. 'Matin chime' means early morning bell ringing, or campanology!

Hints & Tips: The melody twists and turns through bars 9–14. Practise this slowly at first, marking in any additional fingering that you need to guide yourself through as smoothly as possible. You could also try practising the phrase in dotted or triplet rhythms to even out the note lengths.

Voice: **Pipe Organ**

Rhythm: **Baroque**

Tempo: ♩ = 142

God Rest Ye Merry, Gentlemen

Traditional

The lyrics to this song date back to the 15th century. The title in those days would
have had a different meaning — 'rest' meant 'to keep' and 'merry' meant 'strong'.
Thus, the title in modern parlance would be 'God Keep You Strong, Gentlemen'.

Hints & Tips: Your keyboard probably has a few different march beats.
Try each of them out before choosing your favourite rhythmic accompaniment for this song.

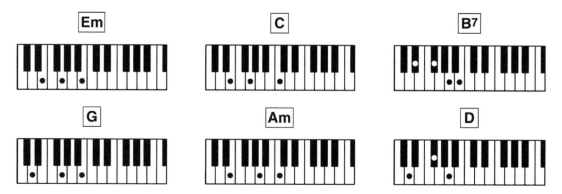

Voice: **Violin**

Rhythm: **March**

Tempo: ♩ = 120

Freely

God rest you mer - ry, gen - tle - men, let noth - ing you dis - may. For

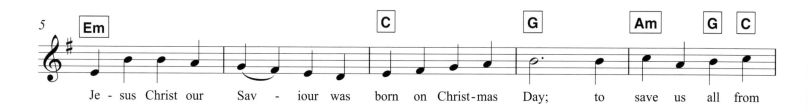

Je - sus Christ our Sav - iour was born on Christ-mas Day; to save us all from

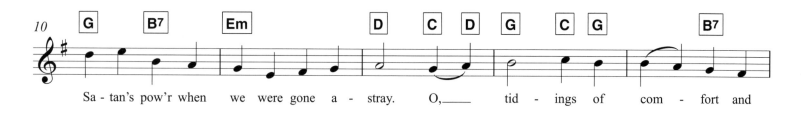

Sa - tan's pow'r when we were gone a - stray. O,___ tid - ings of com - fort and

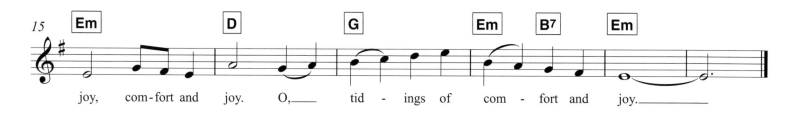

joy, com-fort and joy. O,___ tid - ings of com - fort and joy.___

Let It Snow! Let It Snow! Let It Snow!

Words by Sammy Cahn
Music by Jule Styne

Penned by Sammy Cahn and Jule Styne in light-hearted mood in the 1940s, this Christmas favourite gave Sinatra a durable hit. In December 2003, his version was the 25-millionth song downloaded from the Apple iTunes Music Store.

Hints & Tips: Play this jazzy Christmas song with a lightly swung quavers to create the gentle lilt it requires to bob along.

Voice: **Flute**
Rhythm: **Big Band**
Tempo: ♩ = 120
Swung

Fairytale of New York

Words & Music by Shane MacGowan & Jem Finer

This fine antidote to traditional Christmas songs teamed Kirsty MacColl with Shane MacGowan, in a duet that sounded like a brawl. With its salty lyrics and undertow of Irish émigré disappointment, the song was kept from the No. 1 Christmas spot (and guaranteed BBC TV exposure) under controversial circumstances.

Hints & Tips: This song should have a dancelike quality to it. Keep the melody light and feel as if you are skipping your way through the melody with jaunty dotted rhythms and a strong emphasis on the first beat of each bar.

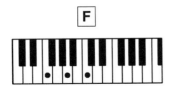
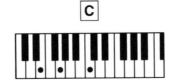
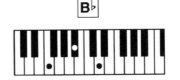
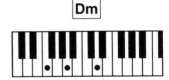

Voice: **Ocarina**

Rhythm: **March 6/8**

Tempo: ♩. = **68**

With a lilting rhythm

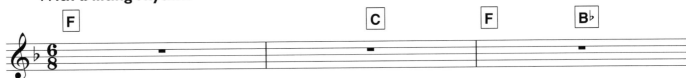

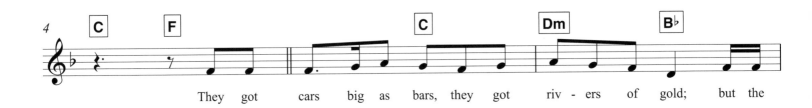

They got cars big as bars, they got riv - ers of gold; but the

wind goes right through you, it's no place for the old. When you

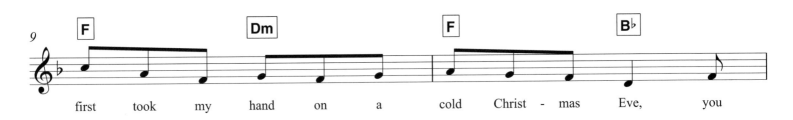

first took my hand on a cold Christ - mas Eve, you

The First Nowell

Traditional

The word 'Nowell' comes from the French word 'Noël', which itself derives from the Latin 'Natalis', meaning birth. The tune is from the 16th or 17th century and is thought to be a folk melody of Cornish origin.

Hints & Tips: Practise passing your thumb underneath your first and second fingers as you would do in the scale of C major (starting with your right-hand thumb on C) to help achieve a smooth melodic line in the verse of this song.

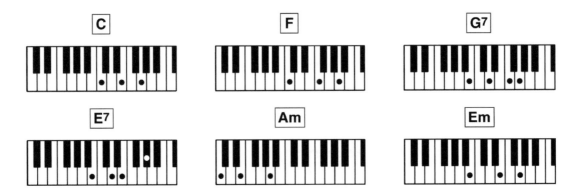

Voice: **Harpsichord**

Rhythm: **Waltz**

Tempo: ♩ = 98

Freely

The_____ first_____ No - well the_____

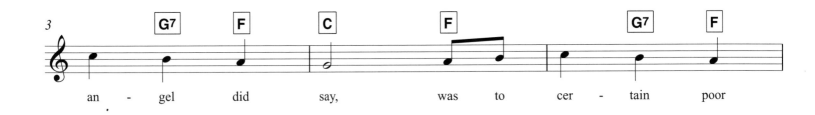

an - gel did say, was to cer - tain poor

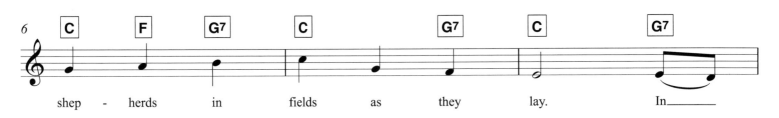

shep - herds in fields as they lay. In_____

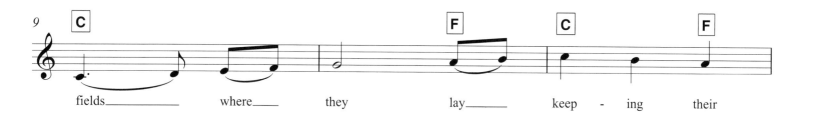

fields_____ where____ they lay_____ keep - ing their

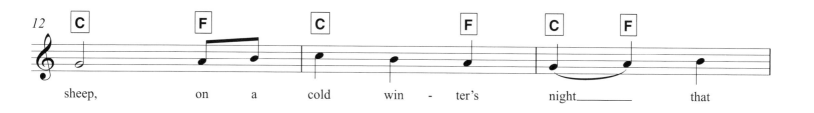

sheep, on a cold win - ter's night_____ that

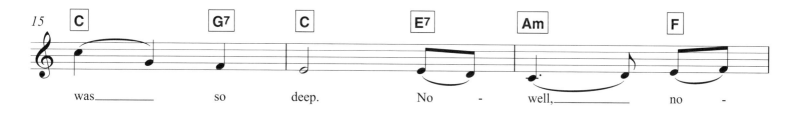

was_____ so deep. No - well,_____ no -

-well, no - well, no - well. Born is the

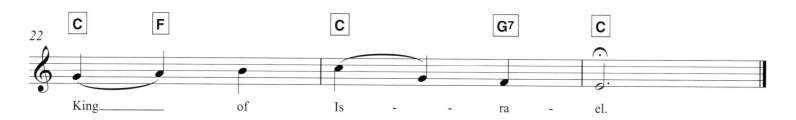

King_____ of Is - ra - el.

Good King Wenceslas

Words by J.M. Neale
Music: Traditional

This carol is about a king, Saint Wenceslas of Bohemia (907 — c.935AD), who braves the cold on St Stephen's Day (26th December) to help a poor peasant. The tune is from a 13th century springtime carol.

Hints & Tips: This melody is based largely upon the G major scale.
Practise it as part of your warm up before playing this traditional Christmas carol.

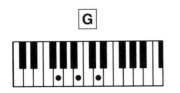
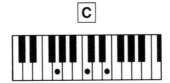

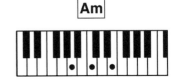

Voice: **Cello**

Rhythm: **Baroque**

Tempo: ♩ = 114

Flowing

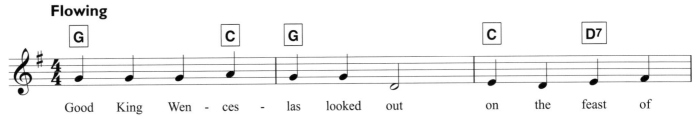

Good King Wen - ces - las looked out on the feast of

Ste - phen; when the snow lay round a - bout,

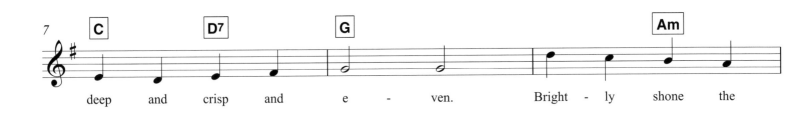

deep and crisp and e - ven. Bright - ly shone the

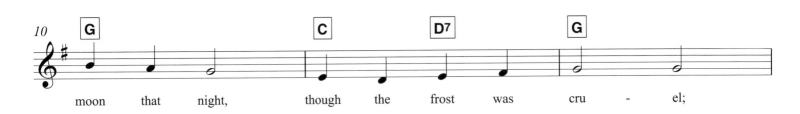

moon that night, though the frost was cru - el;

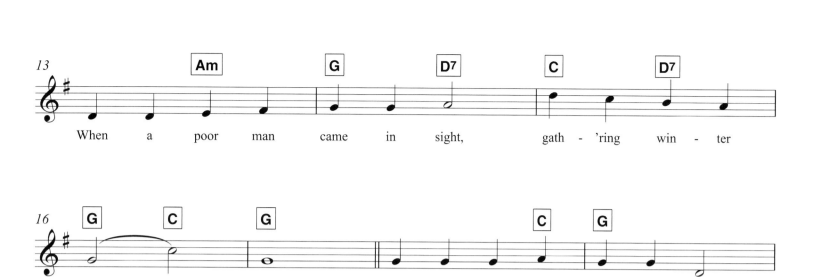

When a poor man came in sight, gath - 'ring win - ter

fu - - el. 'Hith - er, page, and stand by me,

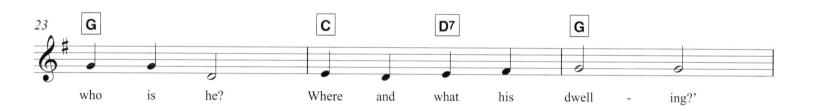

if thou know'st it, tell - ing. Yon - der pea - sant,

who is he? Where and what his dwell - ing?'

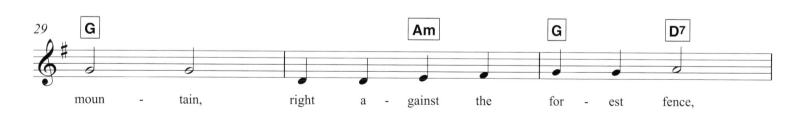

'Sire, he lives a good league hence, un - der - neath the

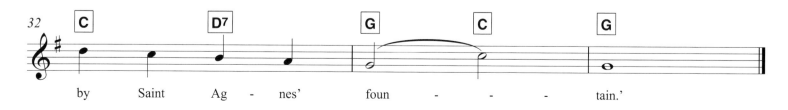

moun - tain, right a - gainst the for - est fence,

by Saint Ag - nes' foun - - - tain.'

Happy Xmas (War Is Over)

Words & Music by John Lennon & Yoko Ono

John Lennon wrote this in a New York City hotel room and recorded it throughout the night of October 28, 1971 at the *Record Plant* in New York. Phil Spector produced, but surprisingly it took some time for the song to attain its now classic anthem status. It has re-charted seasonally many times since 1975.

Hints & Tips: This song moves through several different keys so watch out for the accidentals marked in the right-hand melody.

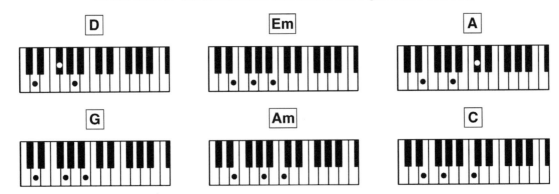

Voice: **Tremolo Guitar**

Rhythm: **6/8 Rock**

Tempo: ♩ = 60

With a gentle lilt

So this is Christ - mas and what have you

done? An - oth - er year o - ver,

a new one just be - gun._____ And so this is

Christ - mas, I hope you have fun.

The near and the dear ones,   the old and the___

young.___   A mer - ry, mer - ry Christ - mas___

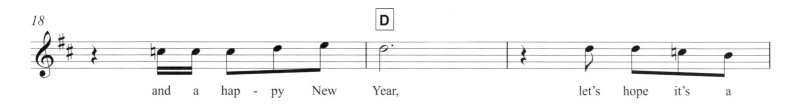

and a hap - py New Year,   let's hope it's a

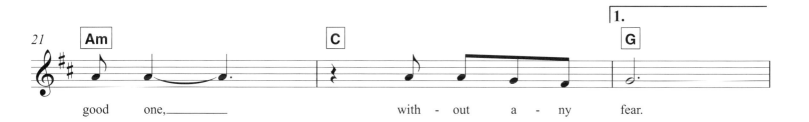

good one,___   with - out a - ny fear.

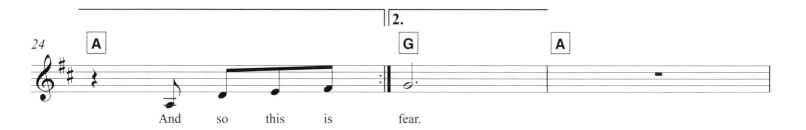

And so this is fear.

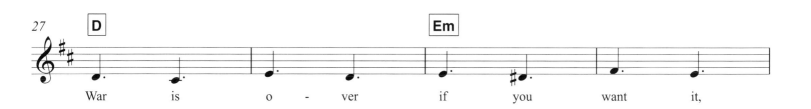

War is o - ver if you want it,

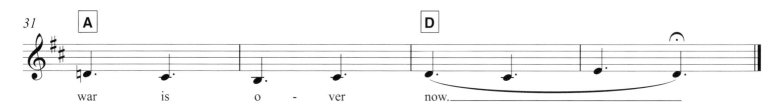

war is o - ver now.___

33

Hark! The Herald Angels Sing

Words by Charles Wesley
Music by Felix Mendelssohn

Felix Mendelssohn wrote this tune in 1840 as part of a cantata celebrating the life of the famous German printer Johann Gutenberg. The words are from a Christmas hymn written in 1739 by the leader of the Methodist Church, Charles Wesley. Ironically, Mendelssohn said that his tune should never be used as sacred music!

Hints & Tips: Try using the 'bridge' accompaniment on your keyboard for the second verse of this traditional Christmas carol to create contrast. You could even insert an extra 'fill' bar as a short introduction.

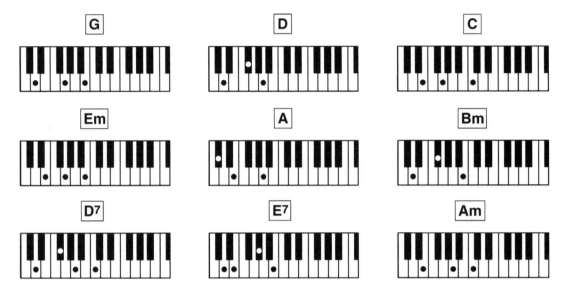

Voice: **Trumpet**

Rhythm: **March**

Tempo: ♩ = 100

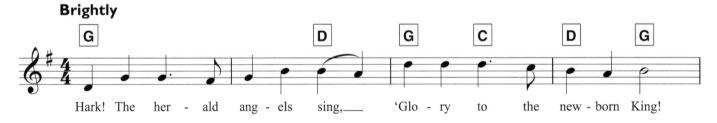

Hark! The her - ald ang - els sing,__ 'Glo - ry to the new - born King!

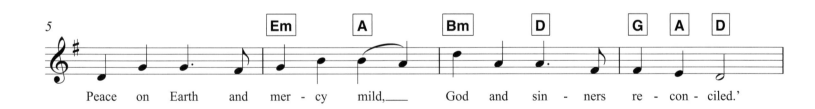

Peace on Earth and mer - cy mild,__ God and sin - ners re - con - ciled.'

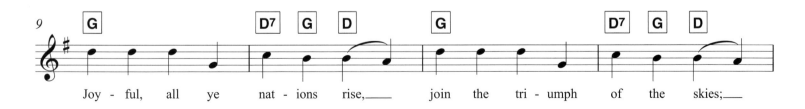

Joy - ful, all ye nat - ions rise,__ join the tri - umph of the skies;__

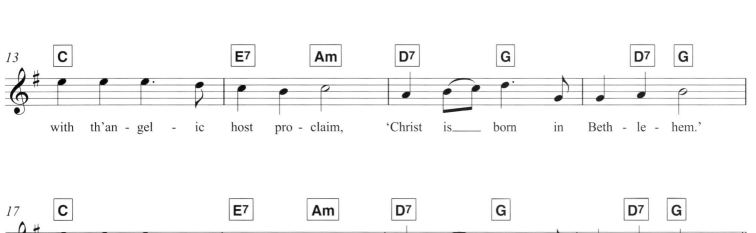

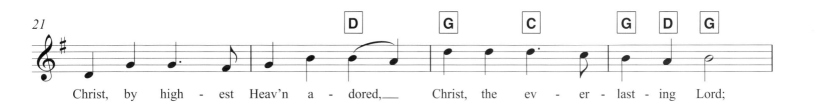

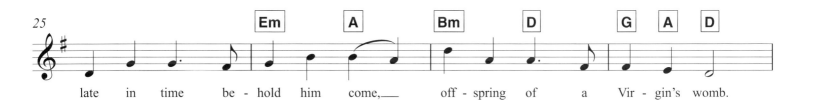

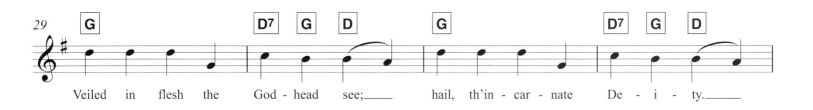

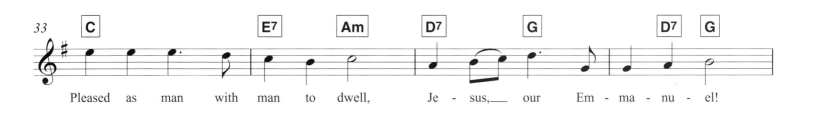

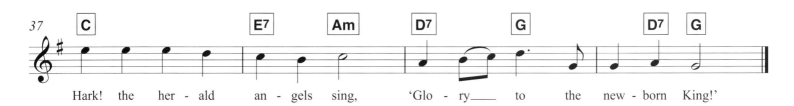

The Holly And The Ivy

Traditional

This carol is rather light on religion and is content to concern itself with holly and ivy plants, which were both favourites of Druids in pre-Christian times.

Hints & Tips: Your keyboard probably has a few different waltz accompaniments. Try each of them out before choosing the one that best suits this song.

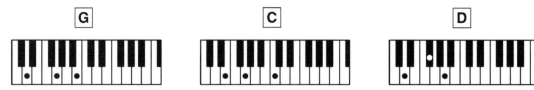

Voice: **Clarinet**

Rhythm: **Waltz**

Tempo: ♩ = 120

Moderately

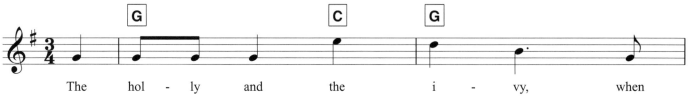

The hol - ly and the i - vy, when

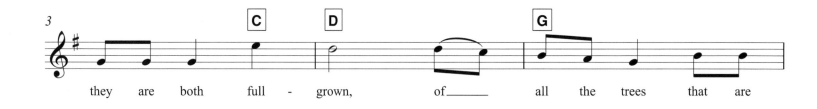

they are both full - grown, of _____ all the trees that are

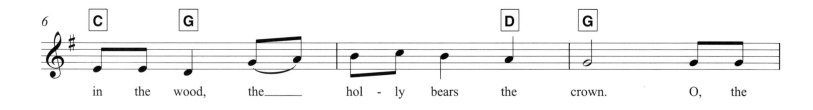

in the wood, the _____ hol - ly bears the crown. O, the

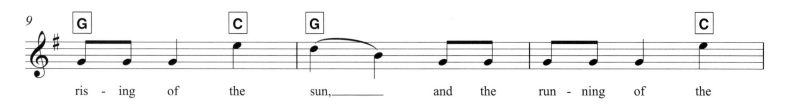

ris - ing of the sun, _____ and the run - ning of the

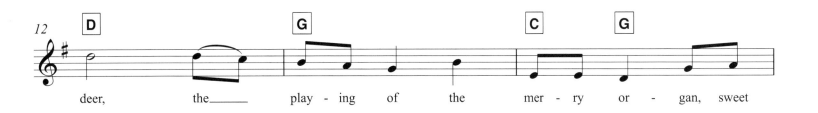

deer, the____ play - ing of the mer - ry or - gan, sweet

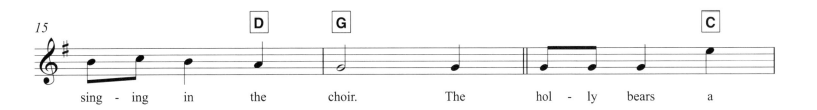

sing - ing in the choir. The hol - ly bears a

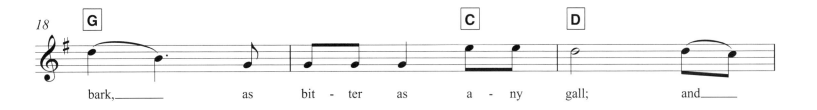

bark,____ as bit - ter as a - ny gall; and____

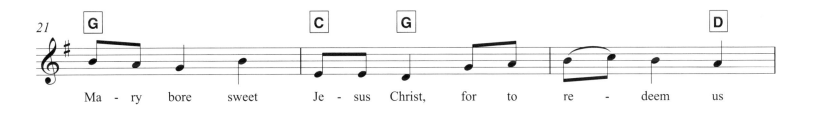

Ma - ry bore sweet Je - sus Christ, for to re - deem us

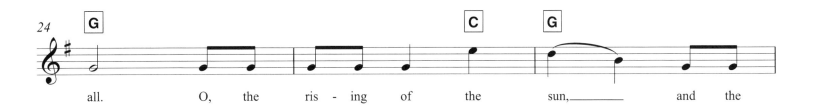

all. O, the ris - ing of the sun,____ and the

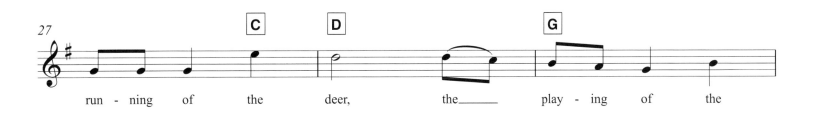

run - ning of the deer, the____ play - ing of the

mer - ry or - gan, sweet sing - ing in the choir.

I Believe In Father Christmas

Words & Music by Greg Lake & Peter Sinfield

Greg Lake's only chart single as a solo artist was a broadside about the commerciality of Christmas. Recorded at Abbey Road and borrowing a refrain from Prokofiev, it featured The London Philharmonic Orchestra and The King's Singers.

Hints & Tips: You might like to select a different voice for in the instrumental solo at bar 17 — a synth brass effect could work well.

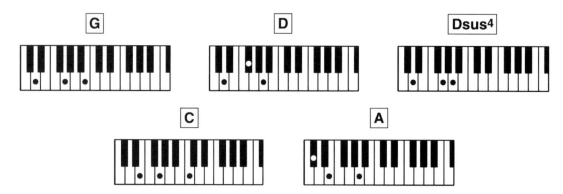

Voice: **Synth lead**

Rhythm: **House**

Tempo: ♩ = 110

Moderately

They said___ there'll be snow at Christ - mas,

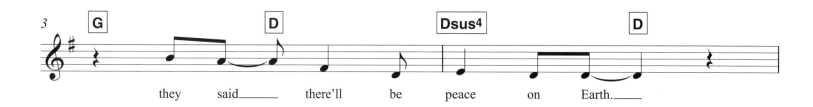

they said___ there'll be peace on Earth.___

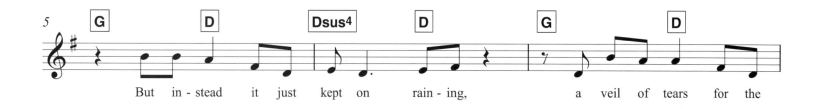

But in - stead it just kept on rain - ing, a veil of tears for the

Vir - gin birth. I re - mem - ber one Christ - mas morn - ing, a

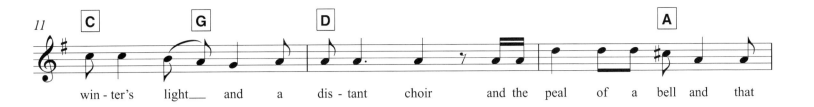

win - ter's light___ and a dis - tant choir and the peal of a bell and that

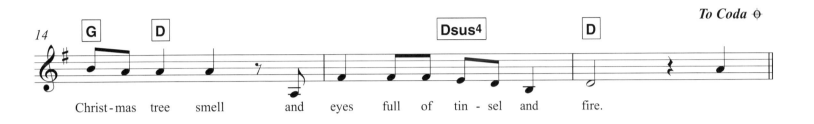

Christ - mas tree smell and eyes full of tin - sel and fire.

I Saw Mommy Kissing Santa Claus

Words & Music by Tommie Connor

A coy, novelty song in which a child witnesses his mother kissing a strange man in a red costume, this song was a UK hit in 1953 for three different acts. American Jimmy Boyd was actually a child, but The Beverley Sisters were already the wrong side of puberty, while Billy Cotton was 54!

Hints & Tips: Rest your hands on your knees to find the curved finger position that will help you move seamlessly through the chromatic passages in this song.

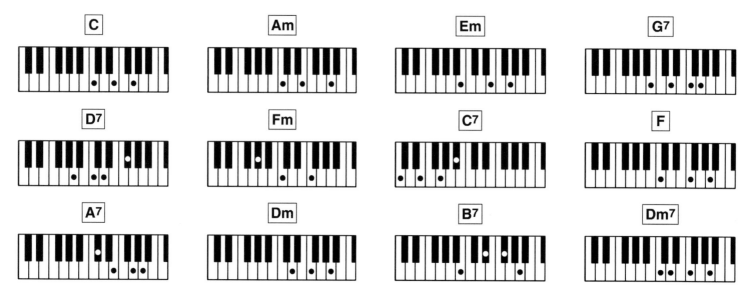

Voice: **Clarinet**

Rhythm: **Country Rock**

Tempo: ♩ = 126

Bouncy

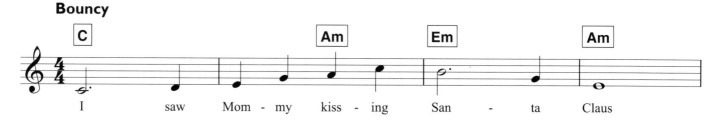

I saw Mom-my kiss-ing San - ta Claus

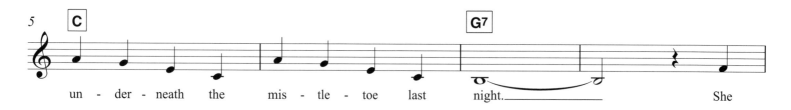

un - der - neath the mis - tle - toe last night._____ She

did - n't see me creep down the stairs to have a peep, she

thought that I was tucked up in my bed-room fast a-

-sleep. Then I saw Mom - my tick - le

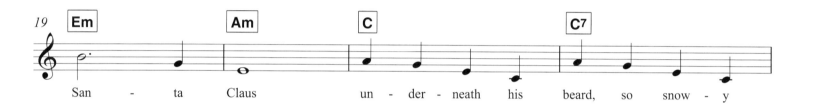

San - ta Claus un - der - neath his beard, so snow - y

white._____ Oh, what a laugh it would have

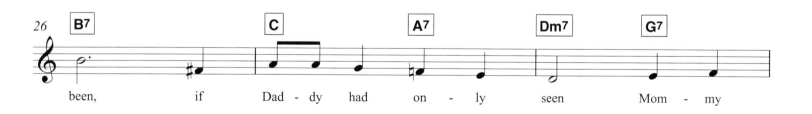

been, if Dad - dy had on - ly seen Mom - my

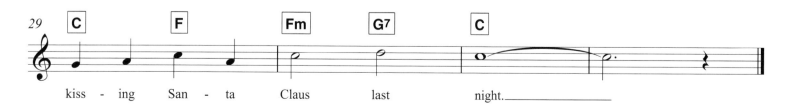

kiss - ing San - ta Claus last night._____

I Saw Three Ships

Traditional

It is curious to note that Bethlehem, being landlocked, has no seaport—this would have made the vision of the three ships coming sailing in on Christmas morning rather unlikely!

Hints & Tips: This song should have a strong feeling of being 'in two', so place an emphasis on the first and fourth quaver beats in each bar.

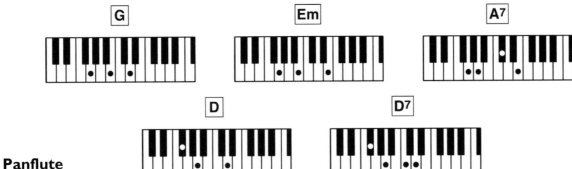

Voice: **Panflute**

Rhythm: **March 6/8**

Tempo: ♩. = 98

Liltingly

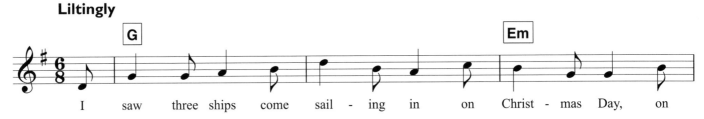

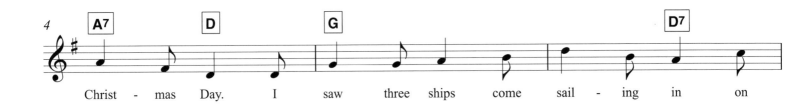

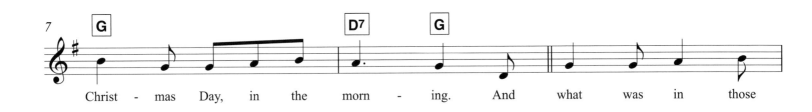

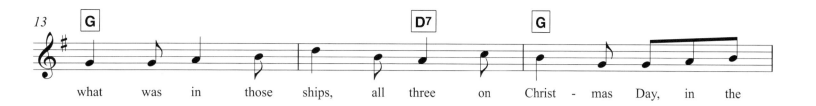

what was in those ships, all three on Christ - mas Day, in the

morn - ing? Our Sa - viour Christ and His la - dy, on

Christ - mas Day, on Christ - mas Day. Our Sa - viour Christ and His

la - dy, on Christ - mas Day, in the morn - ing. Then

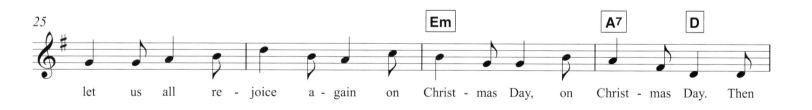

let us all re - joice a - gain on Christ - mas Day, on Christ - mas Day. Then

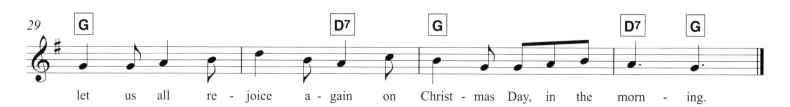

let us all re - joice a - gain on Christ - mas Day, in the morn - ing.

I Wish It Could Be Christmas Every Day

Words & Music by Roy Wood

This 1973 Wizzard hit featured an assortment of Birmingham school children and can be seen as a dry run for Roy Wood's reprise 13 years later when he joined The Wombles for 'I Wish It Could Be A Wombling Merry Christmas Everyday'.

Hints & Tips: Watch out for the key change at bar 17. Play every F and C as sharpened notes from that point on unless there is a natural sign marked (in bar 19 for example).

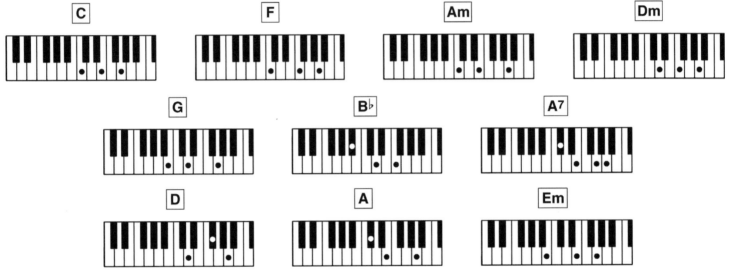

Voice: **Soprano Saxophone**

Rhythm: **Rock 'n' Roll**

Tempo: ♩ = 108

Bouncy

Oh, when the snow-man brings the snow, oh, well, he just might like to

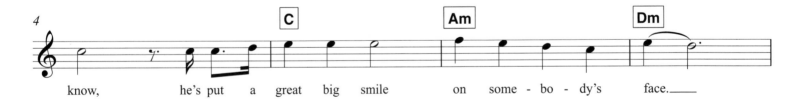

know, he's put a great big smile on some-bo-dy's face.____

If you jump in-to your bed, quick-ly

cov - er up your head. Don't you lock the doors, you know that

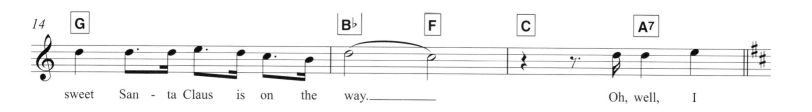

sweet San - ta Claus is on the way._____ Oh, well, I

wish it could be Christ - mas ev - 'ry day,_____

when the kids start sing - ing and the band be - gins to

play._____ Oh, I wish it could be

Christ - mas ev - 'ry day._____ So let the

bells ring out for Christ - mas._____

In The Bleak Midwinter

Words by Christina Rossetti
Music by Gustav Holst

Whilst helping Vaughan Williams with the editing of *The English Hymnal*, Holst composed three hymns for the volume, including this carol. The original folk melody (called 'Crantham' after the village from which it was collected) was harmonised by Holst in 1905.

Hints & Tips: Think about ways you could create a contrast between the different verses. Perhaps change the voice to another member of the string family or add a dual voice, pairing the violin with a lower-sounding instrument.

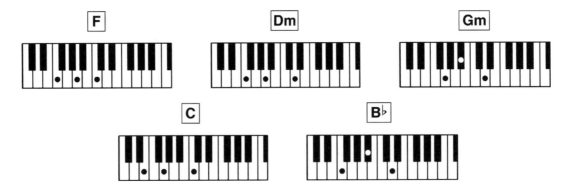

Voice: **Violin**

Rhythm: **Baroque**

Tempo: ♩ = 84

Solemnly

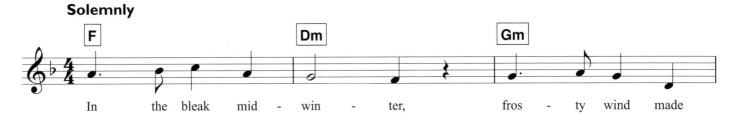

In the bleak mid - win - ter, fros - ty wind made

moan. Earth stood hard as i - ron,

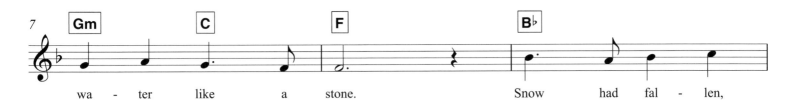

wa - ter like a stone. Snow had fal - len,

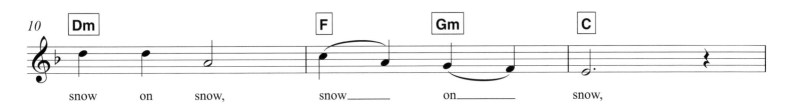

snow on snow, snow_____ on_____ snow,

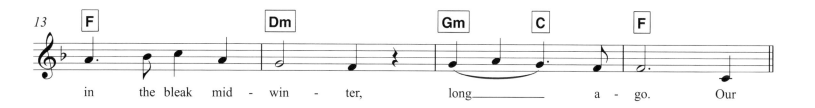

in the bleak mid - win - ter, long_____ a - go. Our

God, Heav'n can - not hold Him, nor_____ earth sus -

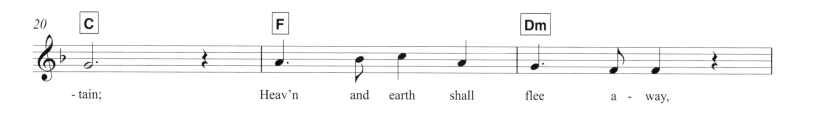

- tain; Heav'n and earth shall flee a - way,

when He comes to reign. In the bleak mid -

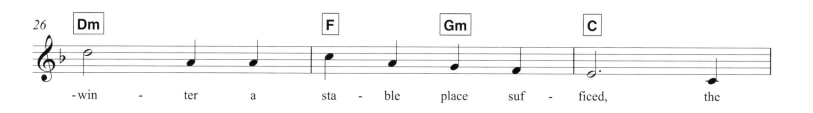

-win - ter a sta - ble place suf - ficed, the

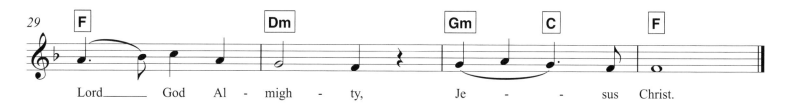

Lord_____ God Al - migh - ty, Je - - sus Christ.

Jingle Bell Rock

Words & Music by Joseph Beal & James Boothe

Philadelphia-based 60s popsters Chubby Checker ('The Twist') and Bobby Rydell
('Wild One') revisited Bobby Helms' 1957 hit on their 1961 collaborative album
of duets, patter and mutual self-congratulation. It made the US Top 40.

Hints & Tips: Swing the quavers in this Christmas pop song to create a shuffle
effect, but make sure you keep up with the accompaniment; no lagging behind!

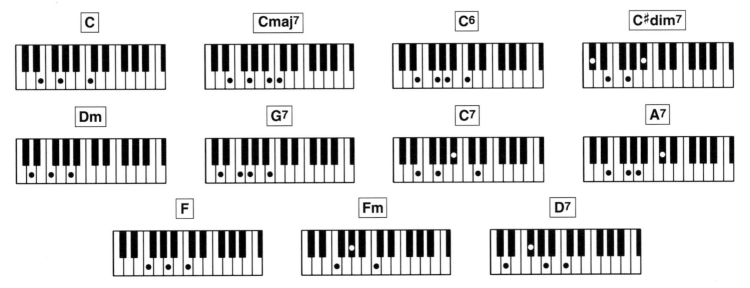

Voice: **Jazz Guitar**

Rhythm: **Country Rock (Triplet)**

Tempo: ♩ = 120

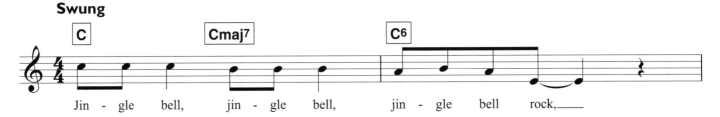

Jin - gle bell, jin - gle bell, jin - gle bell rock,___

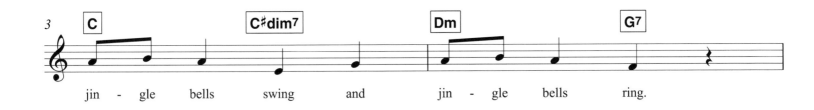

jin - gle bells swing and jin - gle bells ring.

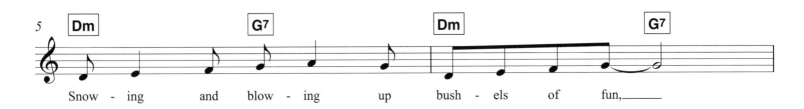

Snow - ing and blow - ing up bush - els of fun,___

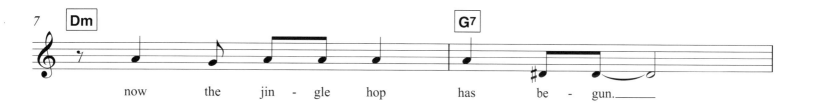

now the jin - gle hop has be - gun.___

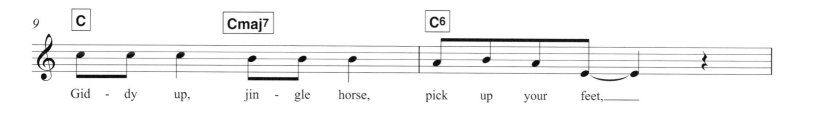

Gid - dy up, jin - gle horse, pick up your feet,___

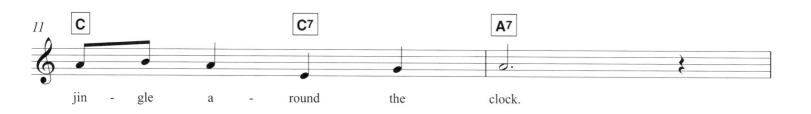

jin - gle a - round the clock.

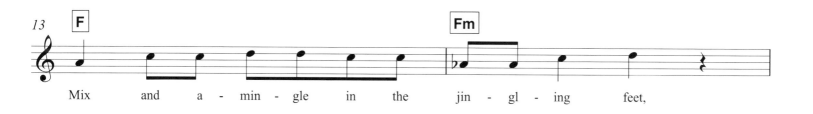

Mix and a - min - gle in the jin - gl - ing feet,

that's the jin - gle bell, that's the jin - gle bell,

that's the jin - gle bell rock.

Jingle Bells

Words & Music by James Lord Pierpont

In a Christmas-themed joke in December 1965, two of the astronauts aboard Gemini 6 offered the following unlikely observance to NASA mission control: 'We have an object, looks like a satellite, going from north to south, probably in polar orbit...I see a command module and eight smaller modules in front. The pilot of the command module is wearing a red suit...'. They then proceeded to broadcast the world premiere of Jingle Bells in orbit!

Hints & Tips: Try out different mixes of articulation such as *staccato* and *tenuto* to create a fun and lively chorus from bar 17 onwards, even though the same note is repeated several times.

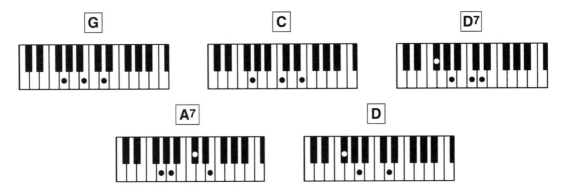

Voice: **Celeste**

Rhythm: **8-Beat Rock**

Tempo: ♩ = 80

Bouncily

Dash - ing through the snow, in a one - horse o - pen

sleigh. O'er the fields we go, laugh - ing all the

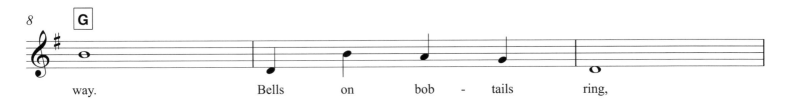

way. Bells on bob - tails ring,

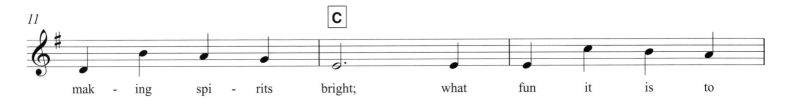

mak - ing spi - rits bright; what fun it is to

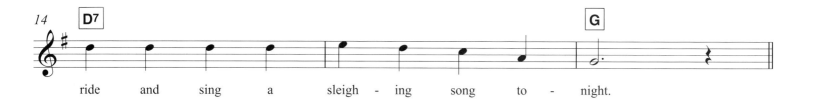

ride and sing a sleigh - ing song to - night.

Jin - gle bells, jin - gle bells, jin - gle all the

way; oh, what fun it is to ride in a

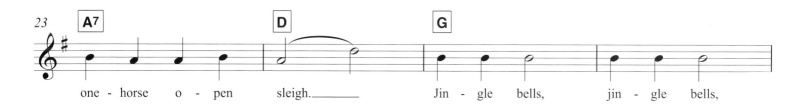

one - horse o - pen sleigh._____ Jin - gle bells, jin - gle bells,

jin - gle all the way;_____ oh, what fun it

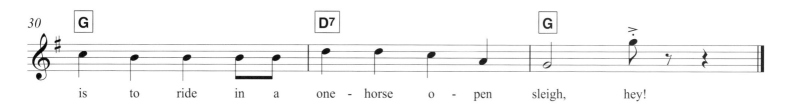

is to ride in a one - horse o - pen sleigh, hey!

Joy To The World

Words by Isaac Watts
Music by George Frideric Handel

This traditional Christmas carol has also been recorded by many popular music artists in various styles, including a ballad by Andy Williams and a dance-pop version by Mariah Carey.

Hints & Tips: This jubilant carol should be played with rhythmic precision. Contrast the detached phrasing of the first 7 bars with the legato lines in bars 8–11.

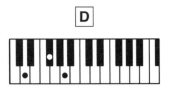
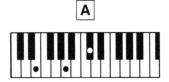
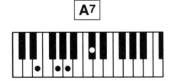
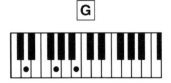

Voice: **Brass ensemble**

Rhythm: **March**

Tempo: ♩ = 180

Brightly

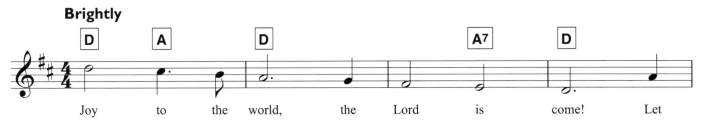

Joy to the world, the Lord is come! Let

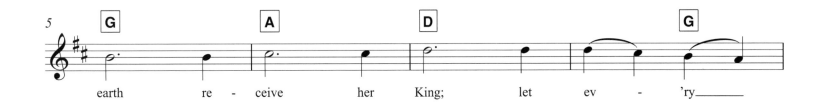

earth re - ceive her King; let ev - 'ry___

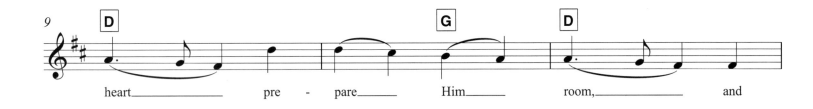

heart_____ pre - pare_____ Him_____ room,_____ and

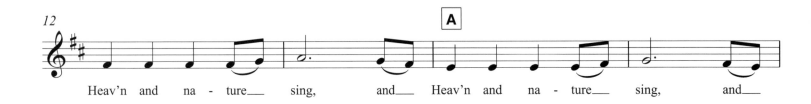

Heav'n and na - ture___ sing, and___ Heav'n and na - ture___ sing, and___

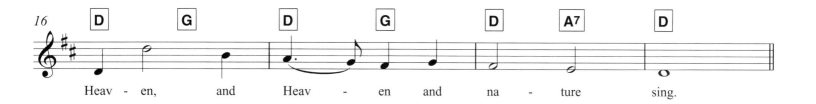

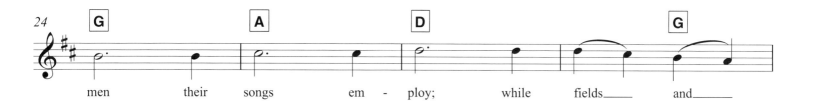

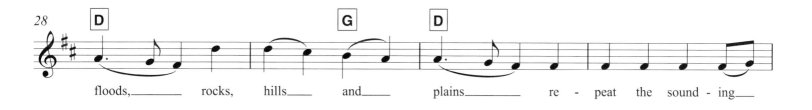

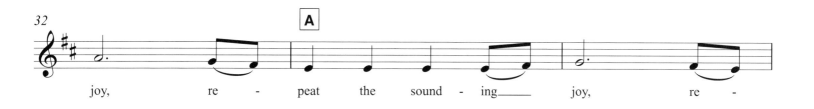

Lonely This Christmas

Words & Music by Nicky Chinn & Mike Chapman

Mud's Elvis pastiche stayed at the No. 1 slot for four weeks and gave the 1974 Top Of The Pops *Christmas Special*
one of its more memorable performances. Lead singer, Les Gray, used a ventriloquist's dummy for the
song's spoken section: it was a lot more difficult to mime speaking than singing, he claimed.

Hints & Tips: You will need to adjust your right-hand position a few times in this song but once
you do you will find all the notes you need are comfortably underneath your fingertips.

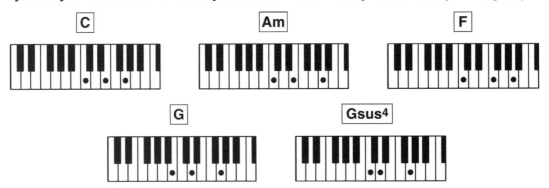

Voice: **Tenor Saxophone**

Rhythm: **6/8 Rock**

Tempo: ♩. = 68

Steadily

Ooh,_____

ooh._____

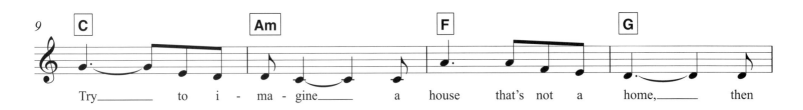

Try____ to i-ma-gine____ a house that's not a home,____ then

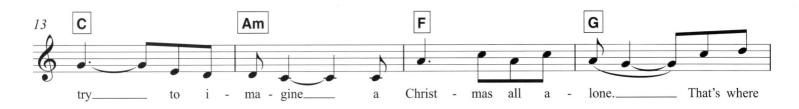

try____ to i-ma-gine____ a Christ-mas all a-lone.____ That's where

I'll be____ since you left me,____ my tears could melt the snow.____ What can

I do____ with - out you?____ I've got no place, no place to go. It - 'll be

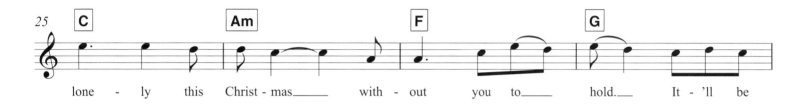

lone - ly this Christ - mas____ with - out you to____ hold.__ It - 'll be

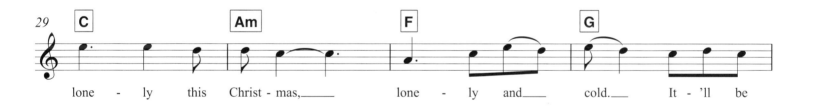

lone - ly this Christ - mas,____ lone - ly and__ cold.__ It - 'll be

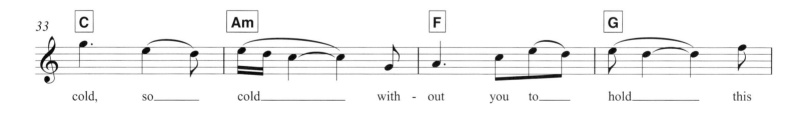

cold, so____ cold_____ with - out you to____ hold_____ this

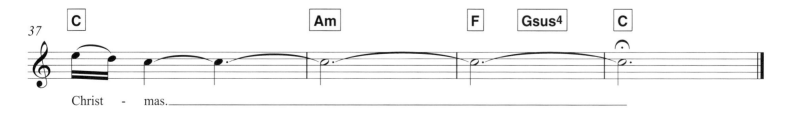

Christ - mas._____

Merry Xmas Everybody

Words & Music by Neville Holder & James Lea

One of the great festive rock songs and an indestructible party hit, Slade's Christmas song held the No. 1 spot for five weeks at the end of 1973. In 2002, Noel Gallagher recorded a version for the Warchild charity album *ILove*.

Hints & Tips: The melody transcribed here has been simplified and the rhythm straightened into crotchets. Of course, you can use your own stylistic licence to waver from this and add character and zest to your performance.

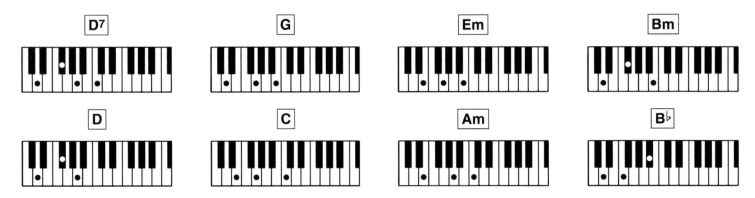

Voice: **Electic guitar**

Rhythm: **Rock 'n' Roll**

Tempo: ♩ = 120

Brightly

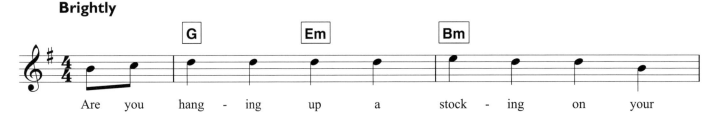

Are you hang - ing up a stock - ing on your

wall? It's the time that ev - 'ry

San - ta has a ball. Does he

ride a red - nosed rein - deer? Does it 'ton - up' on his

sleigh?___ Do the fair - ies keep him so - ber for a day?___

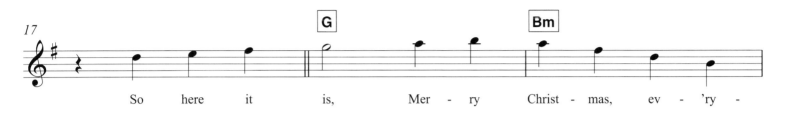

So here it is, Mer - ry Christ - mas, ev - 'ry -

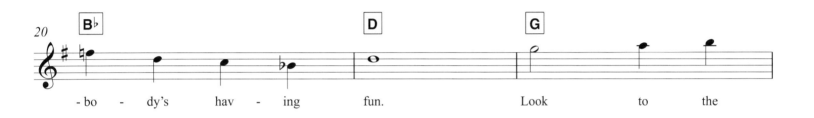

- bo - dy's hav - ing fun. Look to the

fu - ture, now, it's on - ly just be - gun._____

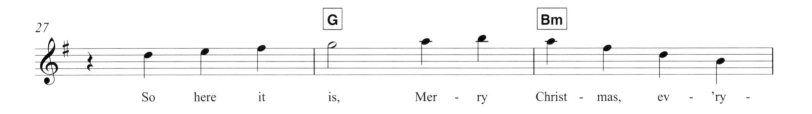

So here it is, Mer - ry Christ - mas, ev - 'ry -

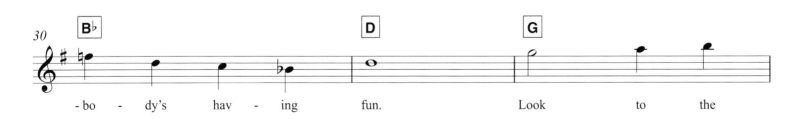

- bo - dy's hav - ing fun. Look to the

molto rit.

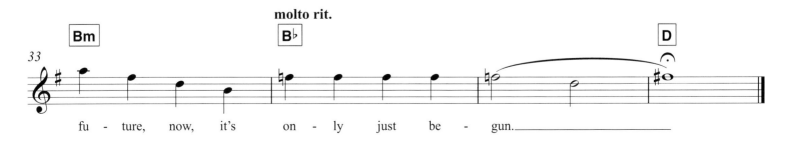

fu - ture, now, it's on - ly just be - gun._____

O Christmas Tree (O Tannenbaum)

Traditional

This is a 16th century folk tune, harmonised in 1824 by Ernst Anshütz. The words are loosely translated from the original version. The tune is also used as the melody for the British Labour Party's song 'The Red Flag'.

Hints & Tips: Exaggerate the dotted quaver-semiquaver rhythms in this jaunty Christmas carol. You might find it helpful to divide each crotchet beat into four semiquavers by gently tapping the keyboard with each of your four fingers in turn, taking care to ensure the semiquaver sounds at the same time as your little finger.

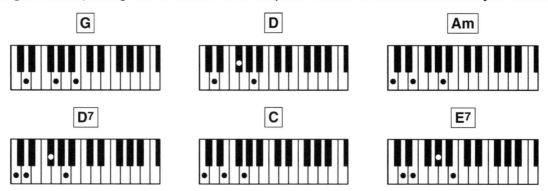

Voice: **Accordion**

Rhythm: **Vienna Waltz**

Tempo: ♩ = 84

Moderately

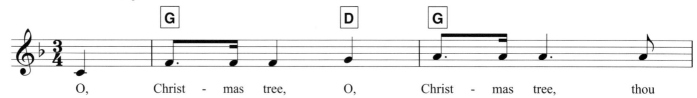

O, Christ - mas tree, O, Christ - mas tree, thou

tree most fair and love - ly! O, Christ - mas tree, O,

Christ - mas tree, thou tree most fair and love - ly! The

sight of thee at Christ - mas - tide spreads hope and glad - ness

far and wide. O, Christ - mas tree, O, Christ - mas tree, thou

tree most fair and love - ly! O, Christ - mas tree, O,

Christ - mas tree, thou hast a won - drous mes - sage. O,

Christ - mas tree, O, Christ - mas tree, thou hast a won - drous

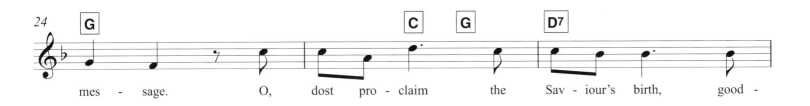

mes - sage. O, dost pro - claim the Sav - iour's birth, good -

-will to men and peace on Earth. O, Christ - mas tree, O,

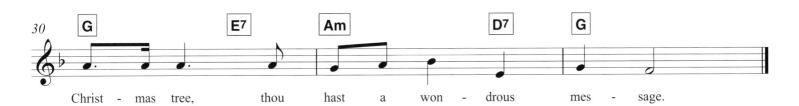

Christ - mas tree, thou hast a won - drous mes - sage.

O Come, All Ye Faithful

Words & Music by John Francis Wade

Possibly the most famous of all Christmas carols, this tune can often be heard with the alternative words 'Why are we waiting...'! It is believed to have been written by John Francis Wade, a Catholic refugee living in Northern France.

Hints & Tips: Reduce the dynamic at bar 13 and *crescendo* (grow in volume) until the final phrase at bar 17.
If you are singing along, watch out for the second verse; make sure you place each syllable
correctly as the rhythms are slightly different to the first verse.

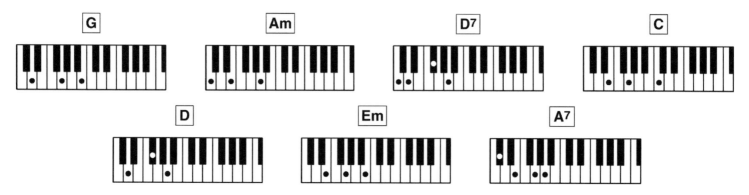

Voice: **Trumpet**

Rhythm: **March**

Tempo: **= 92**

Majestically

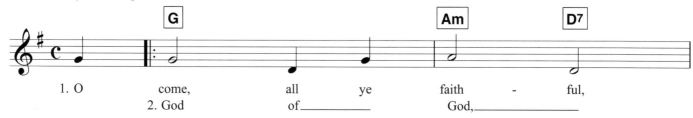

1. O come, all ye faith - ful,
2. God of God,

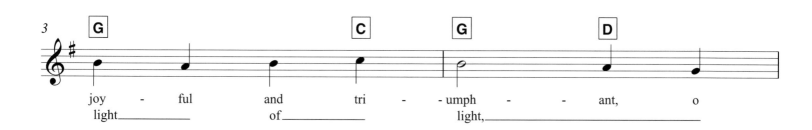

joy - ful and tri - umph - ant, o
light of light,

come ye, o come ye to
lo, he ab - hors not the

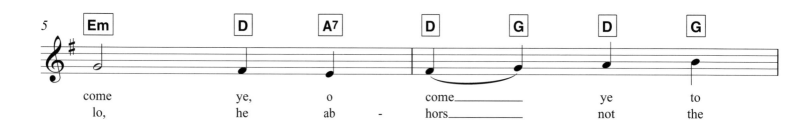

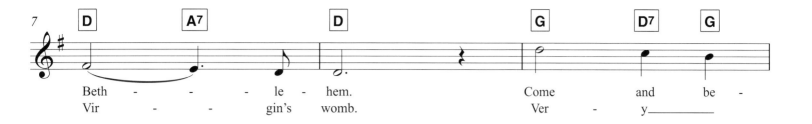

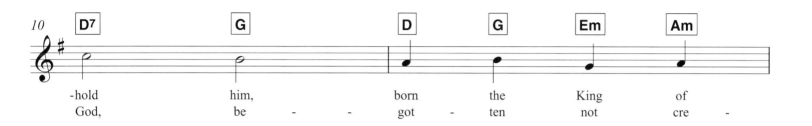

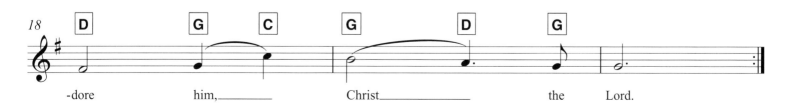

O Little Town Of Bethlehem

Words by Phillips Brooks
Music by Lewis Redner

The English village of Forest Green lies almost equidistant between Dorking, Guildford and Horsham. It was here that Vaughan Williams collected the folk song 'Forest Green' that became the melody for this carol.

Hints & Tips: This is another occasion when it would be wise to use the scale and arpeggio of the key of the piece — F major in this case — as part of your warm up.

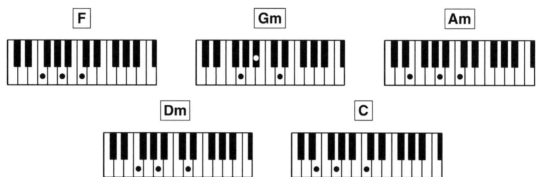

Voice: **Pipe Organ**

Rhythm: **Baroque**

Tempo: ♩ = 108

Freely

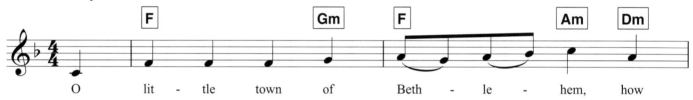

O lit - tle town of Beth - le - hem, how

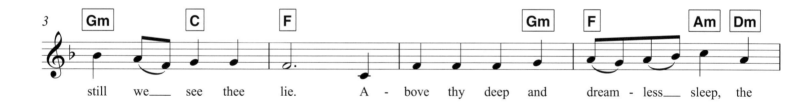

still we___ see thee lie. A - bove thy deep and dream - less___ sleep, the

si - lent___ stars go by. Yet___ in the dark___ streets___

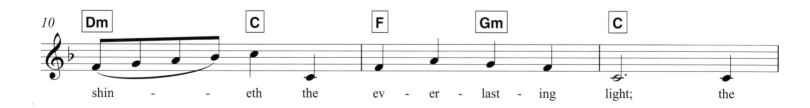

shin - - eth the ev - er - last - ing light; the

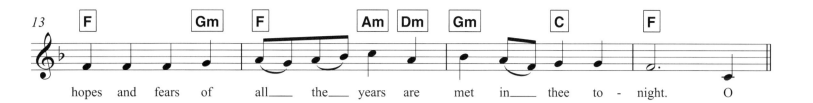

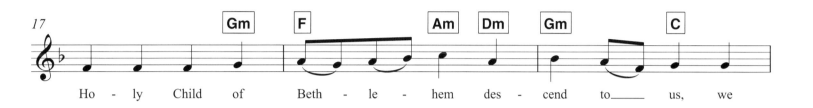

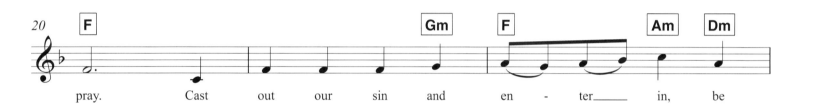

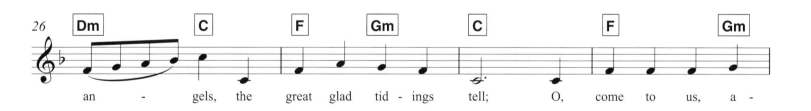

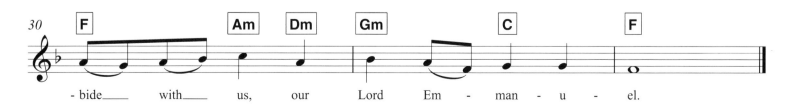

Once In Royal David's City

Words by Cecil Alexander
Music by Henry Gauntlett

The city in the title is, of course, Bethlehem. King David was the second king of the United Kingdom of Israel, approximately a millennium before Christ. The words to the carol were written by Cecil Frances Humphreys-Alexander, a bishop's wife.

Hints & Tips: Play the first verse as a solo with no accompaniment before introducing the keyboard accompaniment at bar 13. This technique is used in traditional carol services and will create a serene effect.

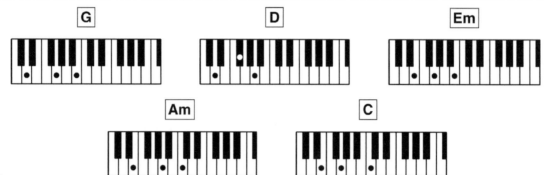

Voice: **Violin**

Rhythm: **Baroque**

Tempo: ♩ = 72

Steadily

Once in roy - al Da - vid's ci - ty

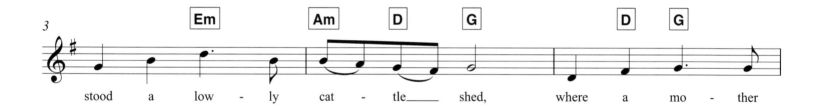

stood a low - ly cat - tle shed, where a mo - ther

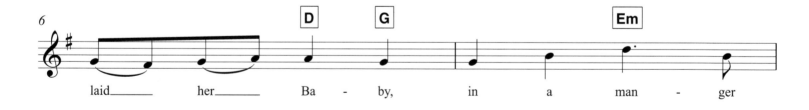

laid her Ba - by, in a man - ger

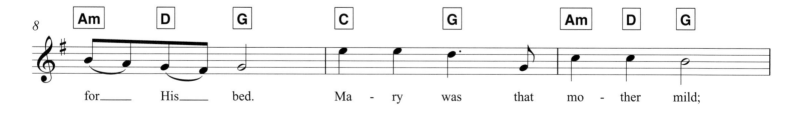

for His bed. Ma - ry was that mo - ther mild;

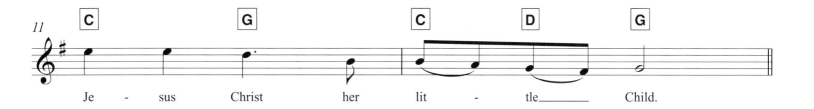

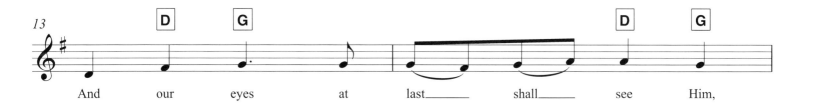

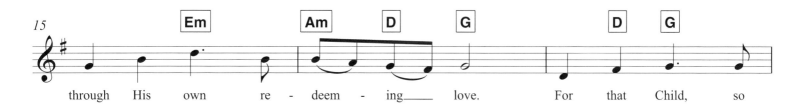

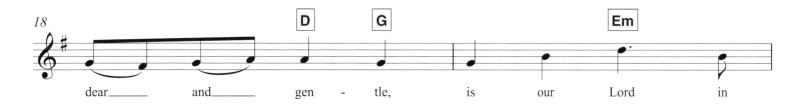

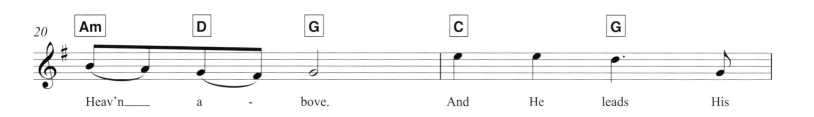

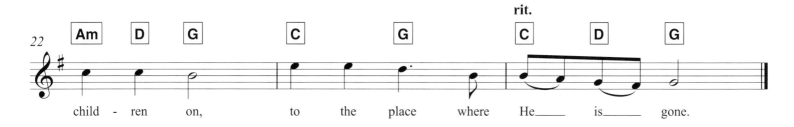

Please Come Home For Christmas

Words & Music by Charles Brown & Gene Redd

The Eagles' 1978 version was a Top 30 hit on both sides of the Atlantic, marking their first release since the multi-million selling 'Hotel California' two years earlier. In 1990, Pat Benatar recorded it for the coalition troops serving in the Gulf War, and four years later Bon Jovi had a UK Top Ten hit with their version.

Hints & Tips: If you aren't familiar with this bluesy Christmas song, look up some recordings online to discover the flavour of this style of music. The most famous versions are by Charles Brown, The Eagles and Jon Bon Jovi but there are plenty of others too.

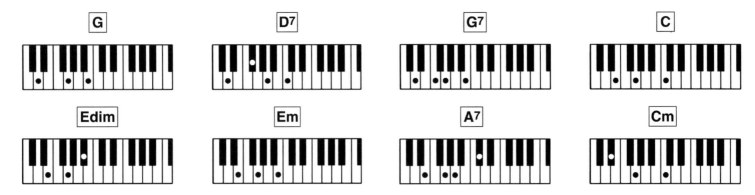

Voice: **Tremolo guitar**

Rhythm: **6/8 Rock**

Tempo: ♩. **= 60**

With a steady lilt

Bells will be ring - in'_____ the sad, sad

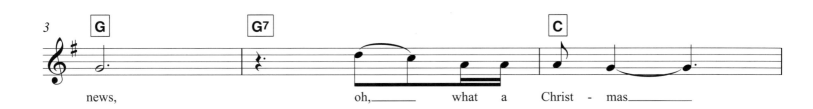

news, oh,_____ what a Christ - mas_____

to have the blues. My ba - by's gone,_____

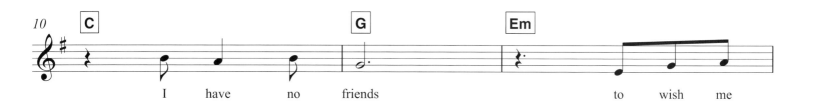

I have no friends to wish me

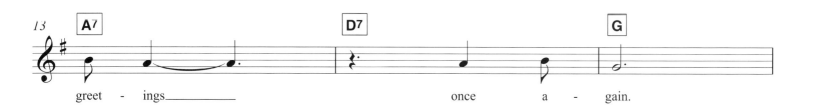

greet - ings_____ once a - gain.

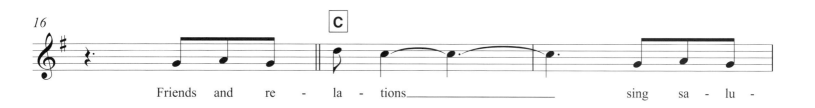

Friends and re - la - tions_____ sing sa - lu -

- ta - tions,_____ just as sure as the

stars shine a - bove._____ This is Christ - mas,

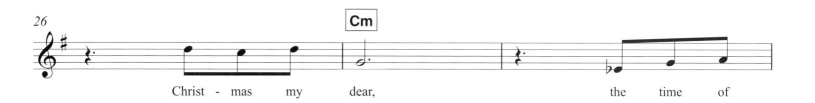

Christ - mas my dear, the time of

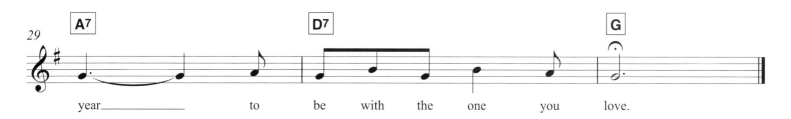

year_____ to be with the one you love.

Santa Baby

Words & Music by Joan Javits, Phil Springer & Tony Springer

'Santa Baby' was the biggest single of Eartha Kitt's long career. Kitt's growling feline vocal mannerisms were meant to make her sound sexy although by the time she played Catwoman on the camp *Batman* TV series, her image was already becoming something of a self-parody.

Hints & Tips: Play this jazz number with a triplet swing effect taking care over the accidentals — sharps, flats and natural signs. Remember, a sharp or flat applies to the rest of the bar it appears in, unless it is followed by a natural sign.

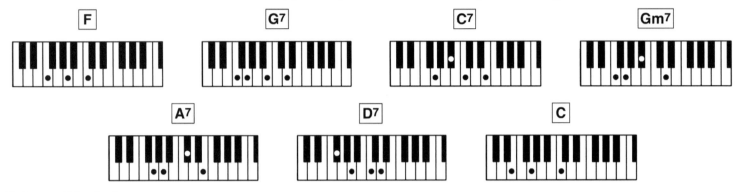

Voice: **Marimba**

Rhythm: **Big Band**

Tempo: ♩ = 88

With a relaxed swing

San - ta, ba - by, just slip a sa - ble un - der the

tree for me._____ Been an aw - ful good

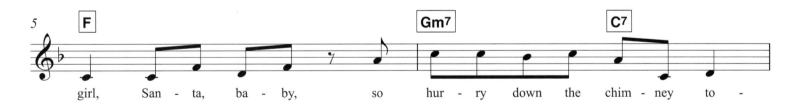

girl, San - ta, ba - by, so hur - ry down the chim - ney to -

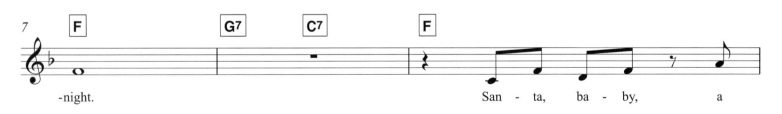

-night. San - ta, ba - by, a

Silent Night

Words by Joseph Mohr
Music by Franz Gruber

It is believed that this carol has been translated into over 300 languages. It is surely one of the most popular carols and was sung simultaneously by British and German troops during the Christmas truce of 1914.

Hints & Tips: This lullaby should have a still quality to it, so play the melody as smoothly (*legato*) as you can. Alternatively, you could select a relaxed, Country accompaniment to emulate the setting of the shepherds in the hills.

Voice: **Panflute**

Rhythm: **Gospel 6/8**

Tempo: ♩. = 40

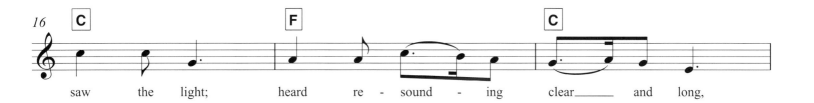

saw the light; heard re - sound - ing clear____ and long,

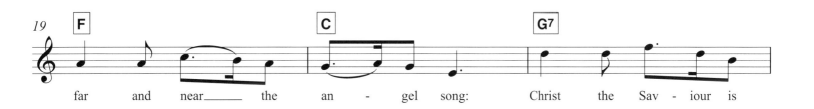

far and near____ the an - gel song: Christ the Sav - iour is

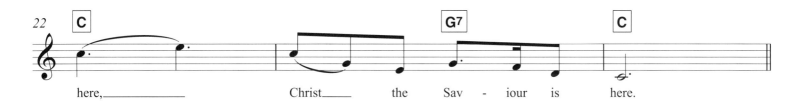

here,_____ Christ____ the Sav - iour is here.

Si - lent night, ho - ly night, Son of God,

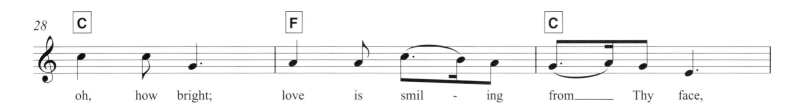

oh, how bright; love is smil - ing from____ Thy face,

peals for us____ the hour____ of grace: Christ our Sav - iour is

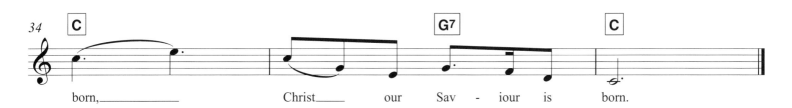

born,_____ Christ____ our Sav - iour is born.

Step Into Christmas

Words & Music by Elton John & Bernie Taupin

Peaking at No. 24 in 1974, this song and its obscure B-side, 'Ho! Ho! Ho! Who'd Be A
Turkey At Christmas', marked one of Sir Elton's very few assaults on the Yuletide charts.

Hints & Tips: There are some large intervals in this melody but there is no need to overstretch
your hand if you can't reach, simply rock your wrist between positions as necessary.

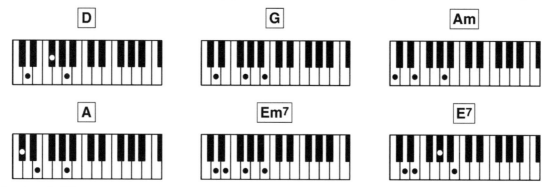

Voice: **Honky-tonk Piano**

Rhythm: **Euro Beat**

Tempo: ♩ = 116

Jauntily

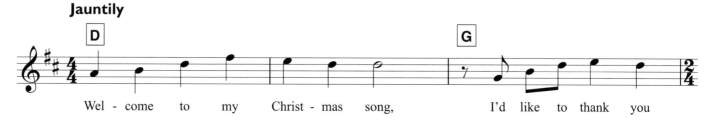

Wel - come to my Christ - mas song, I'd like to thank you

for the year. So I'm - a send - ing you this

Christ - mas card_____ to say it's nice to have you

here. I'd like to sing a - bout

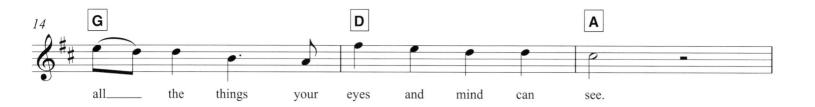
all___ the things your eyes and mind can see.

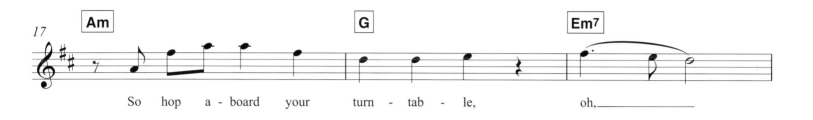
So hop a - board your turn - tab - le, oh,___

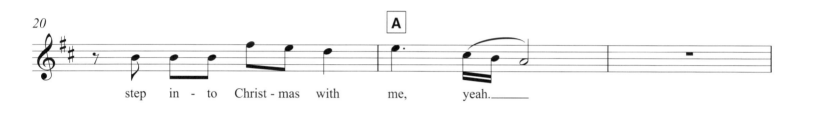
step in - to Christ - mas with me, yeah.___

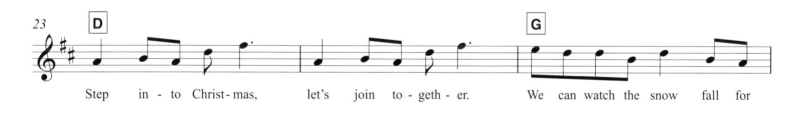
Step in - to Christ - mas, let's join to - geth - er. We can watch the snow fall for

ev - er and ev - er. Eat, drink and be mer - ry come al - ong with me.

Step in - to Christ - mas, the ad - mis - sion's free.___

Stop The Cavalry

Words & Music by Jona Lewie

Stiff Records' eccentric tunesmith Jona Lewie finally achieved a chart hit with his plea for the common man, originally entitled 'Can You Stop The Gallantry?' Its chirpy melody and plea for peace took it into the UK charts for five weeks in 1980/81.

Hints & Tips: A loose wrist and light touch will help you bounce through the right-hand semiquavers.

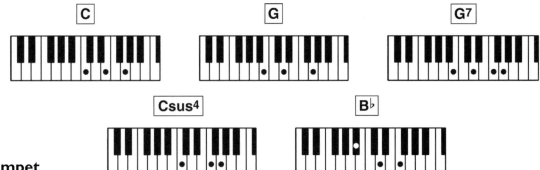

Voice: **Trumpet**

Rhythm: **March**

Tempo: ♩ = 88

In a march-like manner

Hey, Mis-ter Chur-chill comes o-ver here to say we're__ do-ing

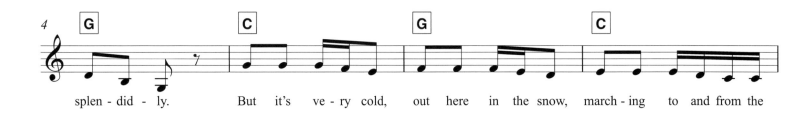

splen-did-ly. But it's ve-ry cold, out here in the snow, march-ing to and from the

e-ne-my. Oh, I say it's tough, I have had e-nough,

can you stop the ca-val-ry? I have had to fight

The Twelve Days Of Christmas

Traditional

This song dates from the 16th century and is still very popular today. A survey taken during Christmas 2005 showed an increase of 9.5% (compared to 2004) in the cost of the gifts mentioned in the song. To buy everything mentioned would now cost over £40,000!

Hints & Tips: Changes in time signature are always difficult to navigate with a keyboard accompaniment. You may find it easiest to stop the rhythm for each 3/4 bar.

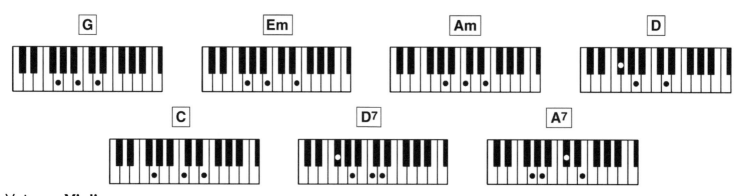

Voice: **Violin**

Rhythm: **March**

Tempo: ♩ = 120

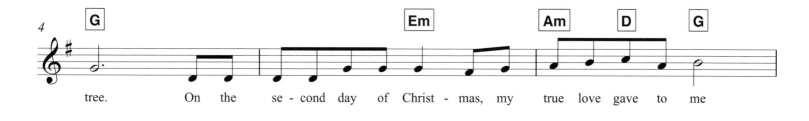

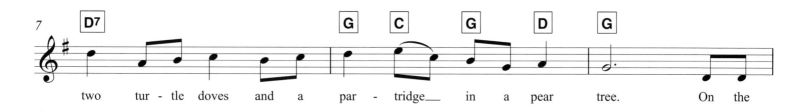

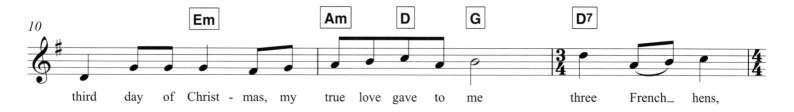

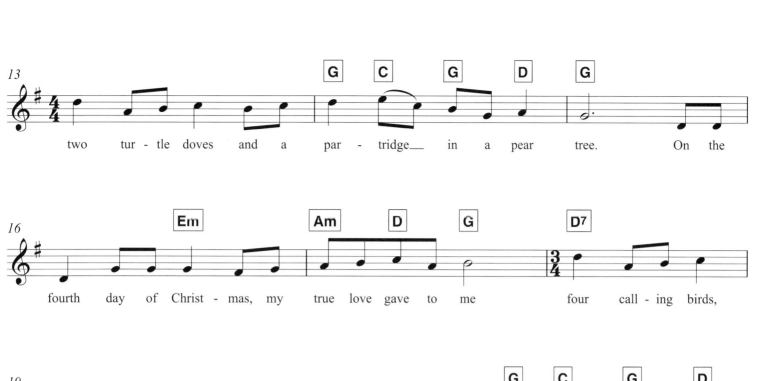

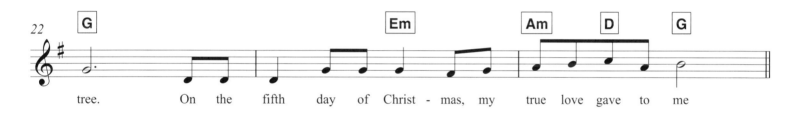
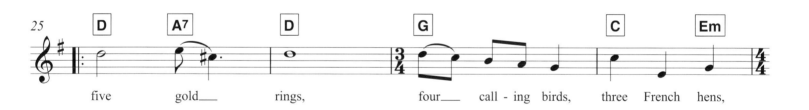
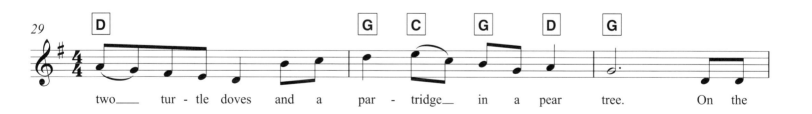
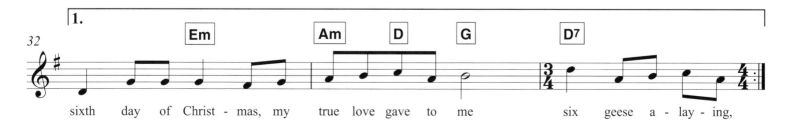

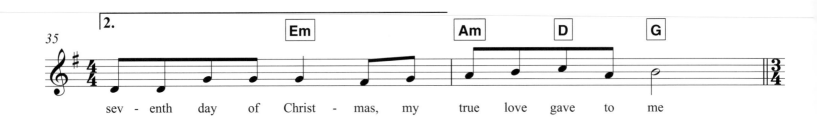

sev - enth day of Christ - mas, my true love gave to me

sev - en swans a - swim-ming, six geese a - lay - ing, five gold___

rings, four___ call - ing birds, three French hens,

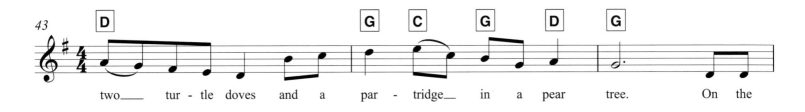

two___ tur - tle doves and a par - tridge___ in a pear tree. On the

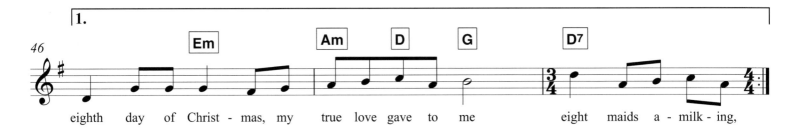

eighth day of Christ - mas, my true love gave to me eight maids a - milk - ing,

ninth day of Christ - mas, my true love gave to me nine lad - ies danc - ing,

eight maids a - milk - ing sev - en swans a - swim - ming, six geese a - lay - ing,

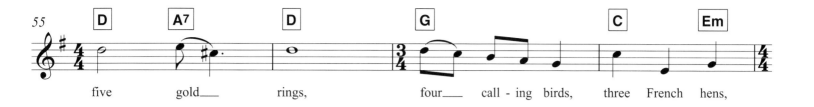

five gold___ rings, four___ call - ing birds, three French hens,

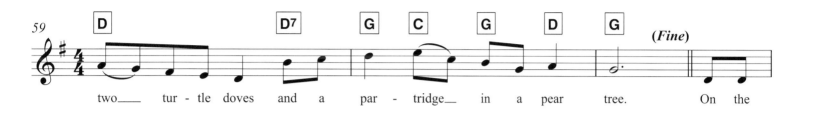

two___ tur - tle doves and a par - tridge___ in a pear tree. On the

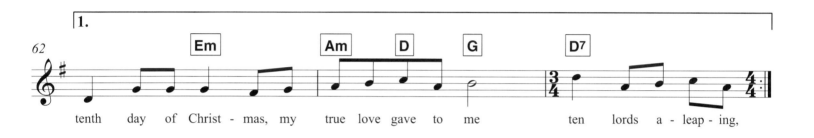

1.

tenth day of Christ - mas, my true love gave to me ten lords a - leap - ing,

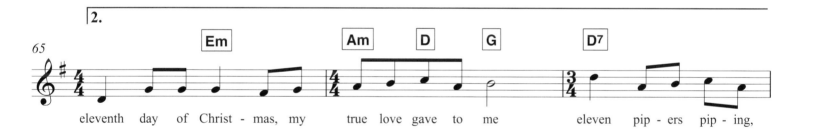

2.

eleventh day of Christ - mas, my true love gave to me eleven pip - ers pip - ing,

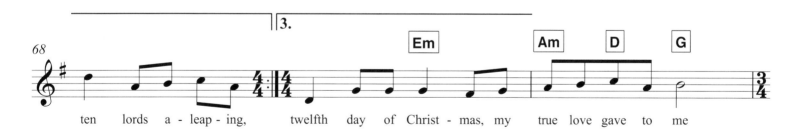

3.

ten lords a - leap - ing, twelfth day of Christ - mas, my true love gave to me

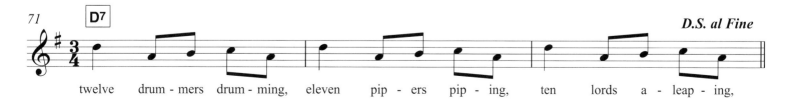

D.S. al Fine

twelve drum - mers drum - ming, eleven pip - ers pip - ing, ten lords a - leap - ing,

(There's No Place Like) Home For The Holidays

Words & Music by Al Stillman & Robert Allen

Perry Como, like this song, was a 1950s easy-listening favourite, and his laid-back US TV show was also popular in the UK. Although the song has been recorded by many others since, it is Como's rendition that remains the definitive one.

Hints & Tips: The melody of this song should tick along like clock-work with only a few instances of syncopation in bars 19, 27 and 31. Tap these rhythms before you play the notes.

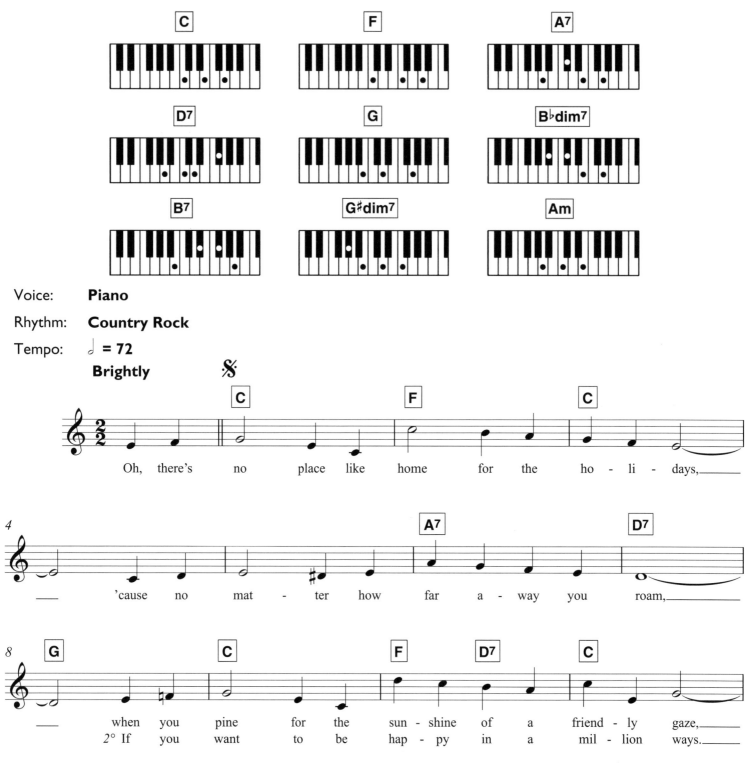

Voice: **Piano**

Rhythm: **Country Rock**

Tempo: ♩ = 72

Brightly

Oh, there's no place like home for the ho - li - days, ___ ___ 'cause no mat - ter how far a - way you roam, ___

when you pine for the sun - shine of a friend - ly gaze, ___
2° If you want to be hap - py in a mil - lion ways. ___

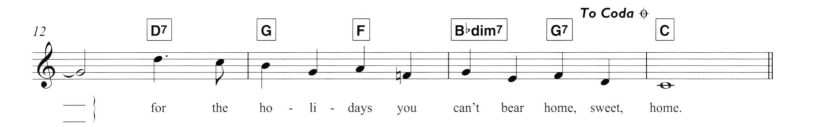

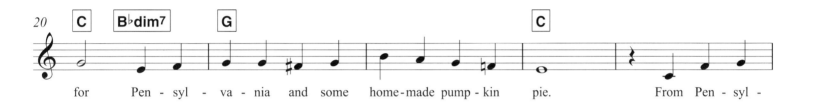

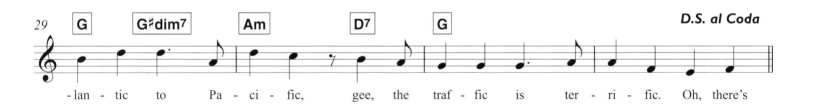

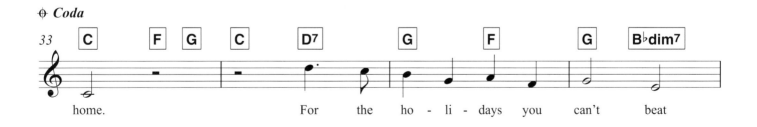

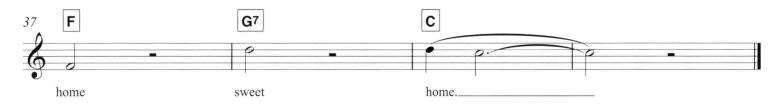

Unto Us A Boy Is Born

Words by George Woodward
Music: Traditional

This carol originates from a collection of Latin hymns for Christmas called *Moosburg Gradual*. The collection was catalogued between 1355 and 1350 and contained hymns that were already 500 years old at the time!

Hints & Tips: Try layering the voice by selecting a dual voice (if your keyboard has this function) as an alternative to the richly-layered pipe organ sound; flute and horn would work nicely for this traditional hymn.

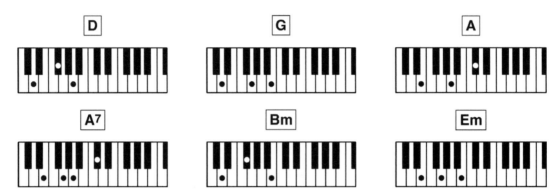

Voice: **Pipe Organ**

Rhythm: **Baroque**

Tempo: ♩ = 104

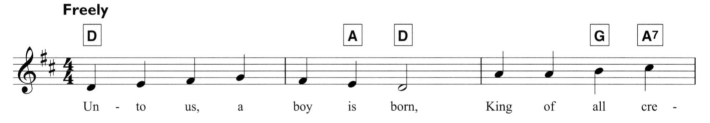

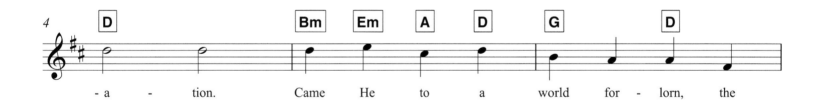

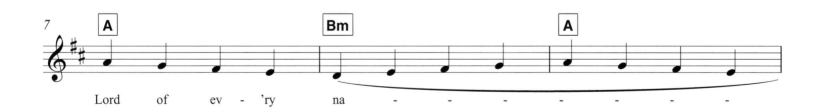

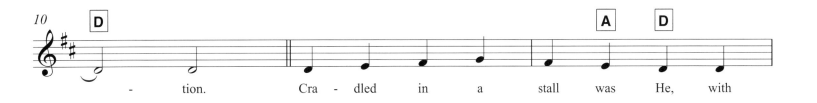

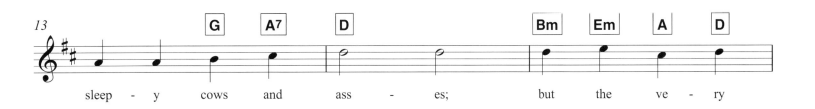

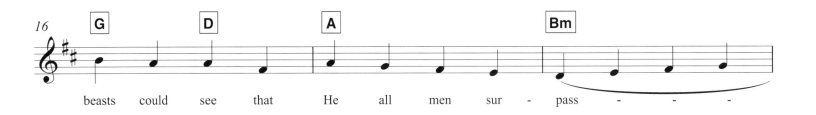

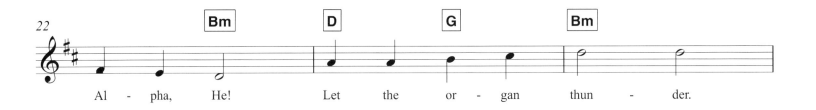

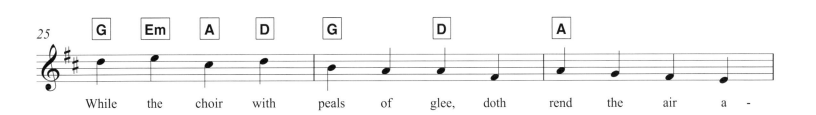

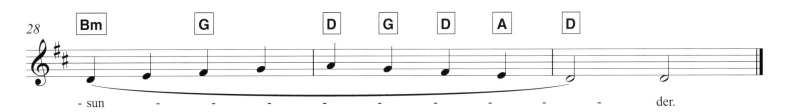

We Three Kings Of Orient Are

Words & Music by John Henry Hopkins

This is an American carol, written in 1857 by the Rev. John Henry Hopkins as part of a pageant for the General Theological Seminary. In the UK, children sometimes substitute different lyrics—"We Three Kings of Orient Are, one in a taxi, one in a car, one on a scooter, beeping his hooter, smoking a fat cigar!".

Hints & Tips: You might like to select a voice effect such as 'octaves' for the second page of this arrangement to create an exotic sound.

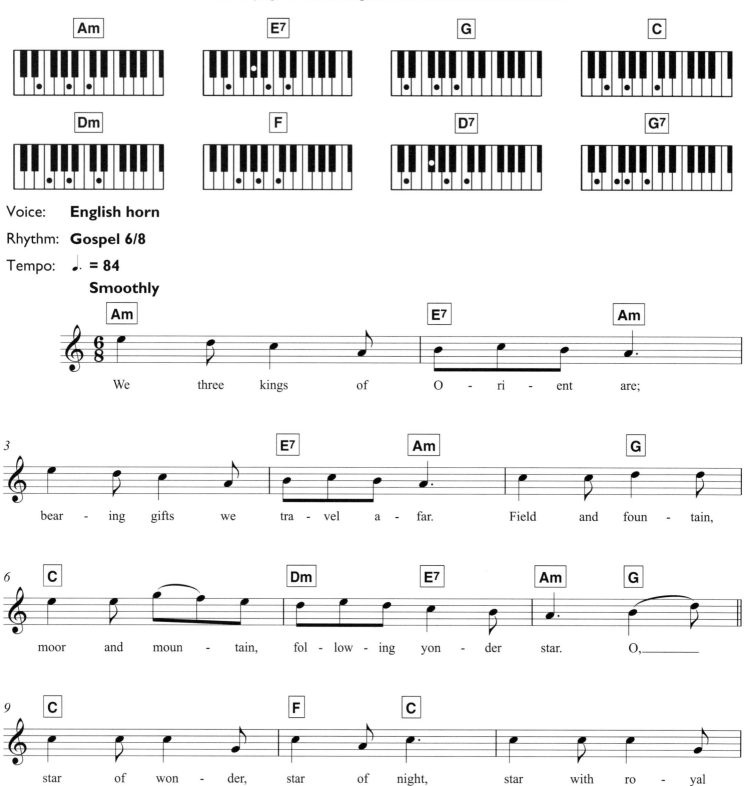

Voice: **English horn**

Rhythm: **Gospel 6/8**

Tempo: ♩. = **84**

Smoothly

We three kings of O - ri - ent are;
bear - ing gifts we tra - vel a - far. Field and foun - tain,
moor and moun - tain, fol - low - ing yon - der star. O,_____
star of won - der, star of night, star with ro - yal

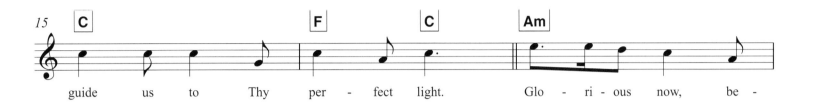

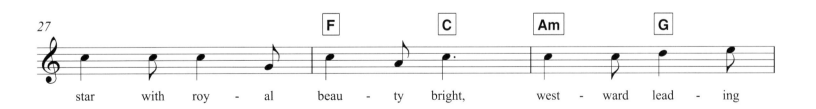

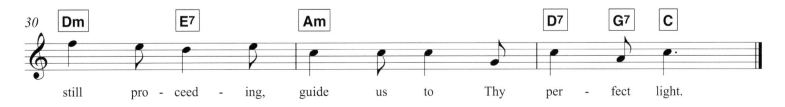

We Wish You A Merry Christmas

Traditional

It is supposed that the carol singers in this song are asking for rewards for their efforts! In their politeness, they make one of the only references to the New Year celebrations in any carol.

Hints & Tips: Play this jolly festive number with a strong emphasis on the first beat of each bar and light quaver movement on beats 2 and 3.

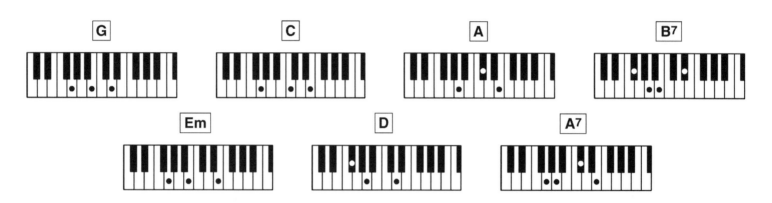

Voice: **Accordion**

Rhythm: **Waltz**

Tempo: ♩ = 142

Brightly

We wish you a mer - ry Christ - mas, we

wish you a mer - ry Christ - mas, we

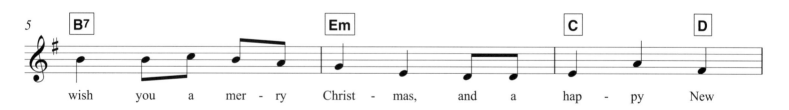

wish you a mer - ry Christ - mas, and a hap - py New

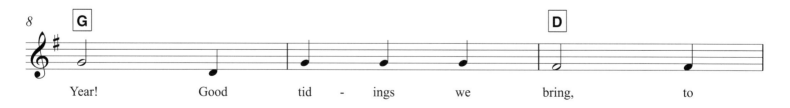

Year! Good tid - ings we bring, to

you and your kin; we wish you a mer - ry

Christ - mas, and a hap - py New Year! We

all like____ fig - gy pud - ding, we all like____ fig - gy

pud - ding, we all like____ fig - gy pud - ding, so

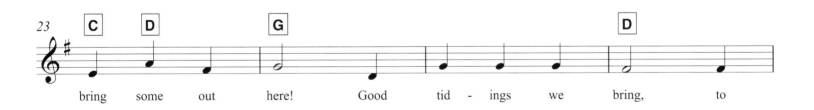

bring some out here! Good tid - ings we bring, to

you and your kin; we wish you a mer - ry

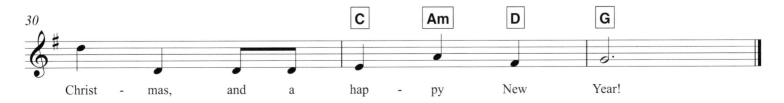

Christ - mas, and a hap - py New Year!

White Christmas

Words & Music by Irving Berlin

Written by Irving Berlin for the film *Holiday Inn* and used again in the film *White Christmas*, both times sung by Bing Crosby, this song remains perhaps the biggest Christmas song of all time.

Hints & Tips: Think about how you shape each phrase of this simple song to tell its wistful story. Consider using dynamic effects such as crescendo and diminuendo as the melody rises and falls, e.g. in bar 5-6.

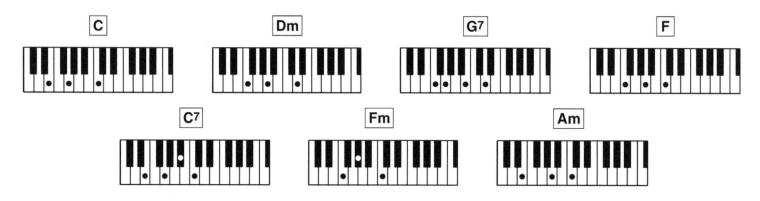

Voice: **String ensemble**

Rhythm: **Soft 8-beat**

Tempo: **= 90**

Fairly slow

I'm dream - ing of a white

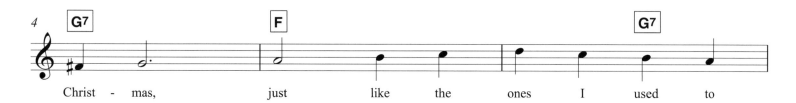

Christ - mas, just like the ones I used to

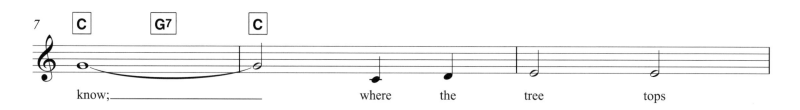

know; where the tree tops

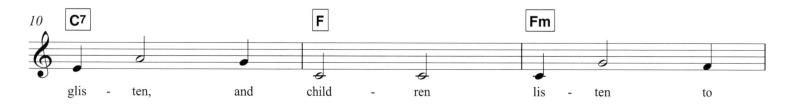

glis - ten, and child - ren lis - ten to

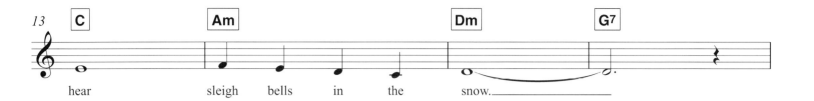
hear sleigh bells in the snow.

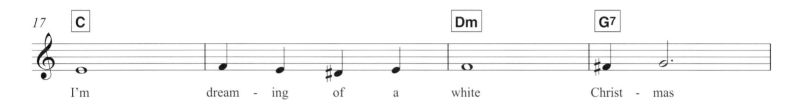
I'm dream - ing of a white Christ - mas

with ev - 'ry Christ - mas card I write.

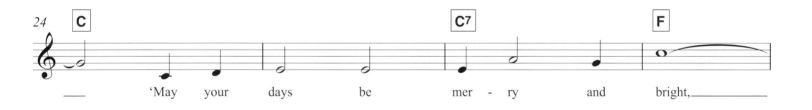
____ 'May your days be mer - ry and bright,

____ and may all your Christ - mas - es be

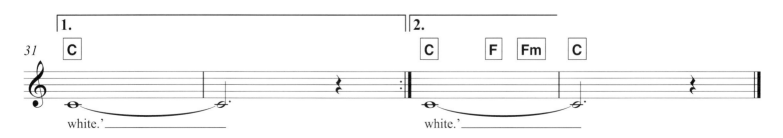
white.'   white.'

89

Winter Wonderland

Words by Richard Smith
Music by Felix Bernard

'Winter Wonderland' was a huge hit in 1946 for both Perry Como and The Andrews Sisters. A melodic song with a witty lyric, it needed less help from Phil Spector's *A Christmas Gift For You* album than 'Frosty The Snowman' had done... but Darlene Love's version on that album is still a classic.

Hints & Tips: You can afford to play the dotted quaver-semiquaver with a relaxed approach to create a lazy jazz shuffle feel to this swing number.

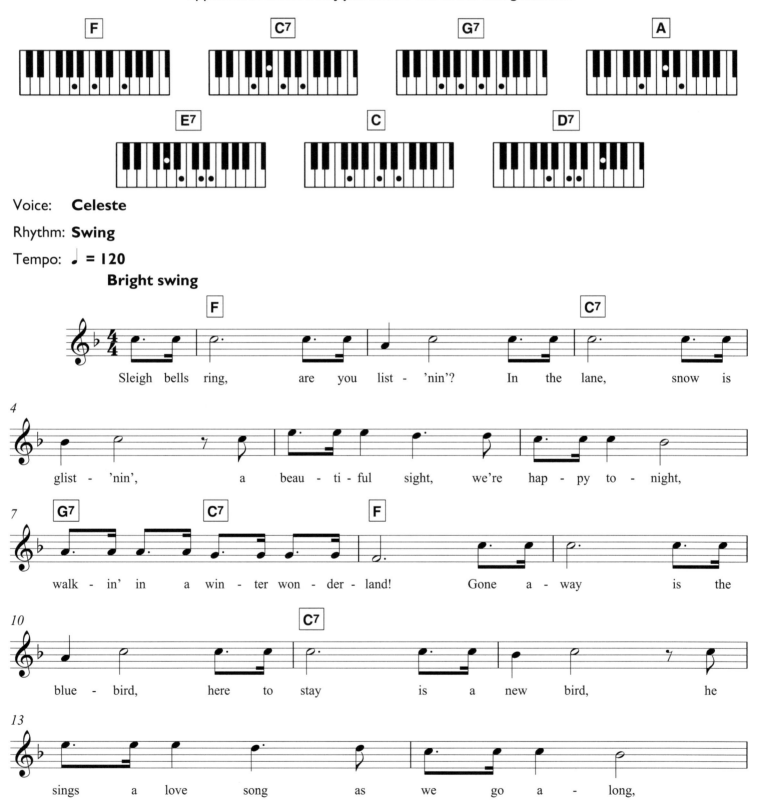

Voice: **Celeste**

Rhythm: **Swing**

Tempo: ♩ = 120

Bright swing

Sleigh bells ring, are you list - 'nin'? In the lane, snow is glist - 'nin', a beau - ti - ful sight, we're hap - py to - night, walk - in' in a win - ter won - der - land! Gone a - way is the blue - bird, here to stay is a new bird, he sings a love song as we go a - long,

walk - in' in a win - ter won - der - land!

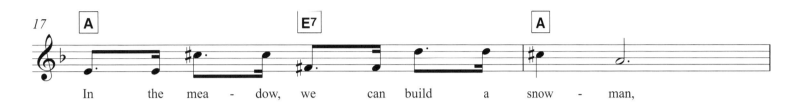

In the mea - dow, we can build a snow - man,

then pre - tend that he is Par - son Brown,

he'll say 'Are you mar - ried?' we'll say, 'No, man, but

you can do the job when you're in town!' La - ter on, we'll con -

- spire,___ as we dream by the fire,___ to face un - a - fraid, the

plans that we made, walk - in' in a win - ter won - der - land!

Wonderful Christmastime

Words & Music by Paul McCartney

Dating from Paul McCartney's post-Wings 1979 solo sessions, this single peaked at No. 6 in the Christmas charts
at the very end of that year. In 2001, the cast of *The West Wing* performed it on TV and it is now identified
as one of the 25 most performed holiday songs by the world's largest performing rights organisation.

**Hints & Tips: Why not switch the voice to 'bells' for the contrasting
section at bar 17, or the 'Ding Dong' lines in bars 25–32.**

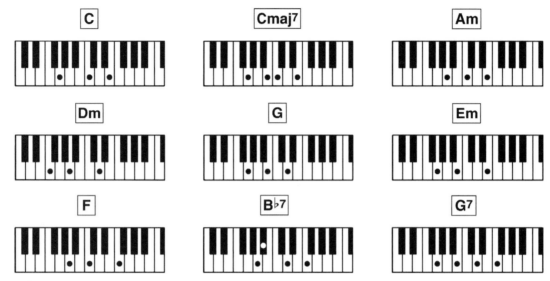

Voice: **Seq Pad**

Rhythm: **R & B (triplet)**

Tempo: ♩ = 138

While Shepherds Watched Their Flocks

Words by Nahum Tate
Music: Traditional

Lyricist Nahum Tate was the Poet Laureate in the time of Queen Anne. He wrote the words for this carol in 1703 and the tune is borrowed from an opera called *Siroe* by George Frideric Handel.

Hints & Tips: It makes sense to choose a traditional accompaniment such as 'baroque' or 'march' for the carols in this Christmas collection, but why not jazz things up by trying to play the melody with a 'big band' or 'euro pop' accompaniment — just for fun!

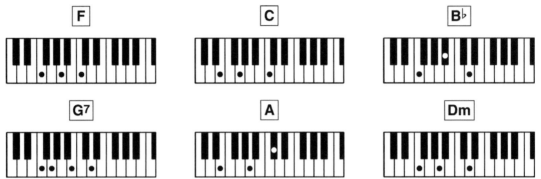

Voice: **Horn**

Rhythm: **Baroque**

Tempo: ♩ = 84

Moderately

1 2 3 4 5 6 7 8 9

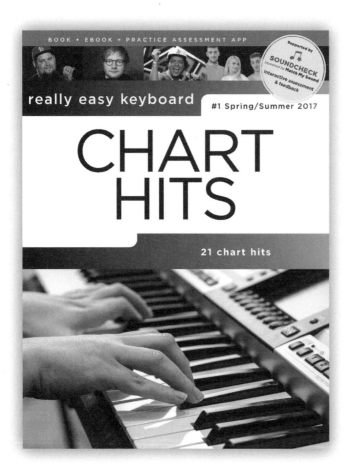
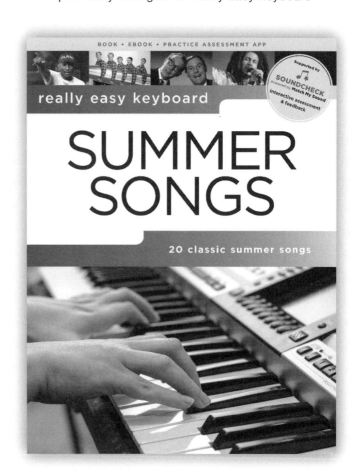